Y0-CDL-240

WINNIPEG
JUN 2 3 2011
JUN 2 2 2011
PUBLIC LIBRARY

The Past is Another Country

Copyright © 2011 The Winnipeg Public Library
Design by Relish Design Studio
Printed in Canada

LIBRARY AND ARCHIVES CANADA CATALOGUING IN PUBLICATION

The past is another country / editors: Tannis Gretzinger
and Janine LeGal.

ISBN 978-0-9869685-0-1

1. Canadian literature (English)--Manitoba--Winnipeg.
2. Canadian literature (English)--21st century. 3. Immigrants'
writings, Canadian (English)--Manitoba--Winnipeg.
I. Gretzinger, Tannis II. Legal, Janine III. Winnipeg Public Library

PS8257.W55P38 2011   C810.8'09712743   C2011-904048-4

MIX
Paper from
responsible sources
FSC® C016245

The past is Another Country

12 STORIES BY NEW CANADIANS

WINNIPEG PUBLIC LIBRARY
2011

This book of stories was produced through the generous support of the Winnipeg Public Library and an anonymous donation from an award winning author who himself immigrated to North America from Lebanon as a young man and found a Canadian home.

—*Tannis Gretzinger, Winnipeg Public Library*

Table of Contents

Preface
Janine LeGal   9

Weyni Abraha's Story
Weyni Abraha, Ethiopia   *11*

Next Chapter Please
Alan Balingit, Philippines   *21*

You are the Master of Your Life!
Iwona Gniadek, Poland   *25*

Myeongsook's Poem
Myeongsook Jung, Korea   *31*

Jill Lin's Story
Jill Lin, Taiwan   *33*

From +40 to –40 C: Why I Want to Write
Deepa Narula, India   *35*

Home, A Place for Sharing
Florence Okwudili, Nigeria   *41*

The Significance of Human Diversity to the World
Nathaniel Ondiaka, Kenya   *45*

Home
Daniela Ristova, Macedonia   *51*

Home
Zulfiya Tursunova, Uzbekistan   *55*

Spring Will Happen
  Rossana Velasco, Philippines   59

Yard Sale
  Jane Zhang, China   63

  Note to Instructors   65
  Story Grid   66
  Questions and Activities   71
  Answer Key   109

Preface

It is a pleasure to introduce to you twelve new writers originating from eleven different countries. All of them participated in writing groups for new Canadians sponsored by the Millennium Library in the city of Winnipeg from 2007 to 2010. These contributing writers came to Canada from China, Ethiopia, India, Kenya, Korea, Macedonia, Nigeria, the Philippines, Poland, Taiwan, and Uzbekistan. As the facilitator it was an honour to be part of such a unique and culturally diverse group. These writers have so many stories to tell and very different ways of telling them.

The writing in this book was chosen in the hopes of offering inspiration, knowledge and perhaps even helpful information to others new to Canada. We also hope that this unique and culturally vibrant collaboration will appeal to others who are interested in and curious about what it's like for those arriving in Canada from elsewhere in the world, at times alone, without the English language, without support or employment.

These stories and poems were produced for our writing sessions, assignments that the participants worked on during the time we met as a group on the second floor of the downtown library. It was there that we had conversations about who we are, where we come from, our similarities, differences, always with the aim of bringing people together, building understanding, demystifying stereotypes, and breaking down preconceptions. The ultimate goal was to encourage all participants to find their voice through writing and to write about what mattered to them.

This collaborative effort gives you a snapshot of the lives of twelve people from very different places in the world. The stories are varied, as are the voices, cultures, languages and traditions. But the 'humanness' and the 'sameness' of each is something that was celebrated both in the class and in the writing. We are proud of what we have put together. We hope that you too will appreciate the distinctive strengths of each writer as much as we do. I have personally been greatly enriched by this experience and have come to know a little more about the wonders of this multi-cultural universe as a result of working with these wonderful and fascinating new Canadians.

Special thanks to Iwona Gniadek, with help from Janice Pregnall and Briar Jamieson, for creating and coordinating an impressive EAL questions and activities section, making this book a unique and valuable learning resource. We would also like to acknowledge Saad Ahmed, a new Canadian originally from Iraq, for taking the photographs of our authors. A huge thank you to Tannis Gretzinger, Danielle Pilon and Kathleen Williams of the Millennium Library for their continued support and encouragement, and for believing as much as we do that the celebration of diversity through the written word is worth fostering. Without them, this wonderful publication would not be in your hands.

JANINE LEGAL, Facilitator, *Finding Your Voice* writing program for new Canadians

Weyni Abraha's Story

Weyni Abraha

"I felt cursed by the sunshine and abandoned by the beauty of my dear home that I always knew was mine. I remembered thinking that I would grow old with the beautiful land but my dreams vanished. The land grew older before me, hit by the bombs. The beautiful trees and flowers were dead and the innocent people were sent away from their homes. The kids were left alone, and the parents were taken away. The home we knew as Sunshine changed its name; it brought droughts instead of rain, and it sent us away to survive in another land.

There are innocent people living on empty land that they love most, but they get nothing except pain and sorrow. As the sun rises and sets every morning, they see nothing beautiful; they hear no good news at all. They wake up to look at every dry tree to see if there is any green change, and they open their ears to hear the shooting of guns. Their eyes are never surprised to see blood flow.

Regardless of the pain and suffering, there are lots of people who would die for the love of their country, and they would never abandon it. However, there are young generations that have lost hope in their land. They feel betrayed by it and would do anything to run away from it. Suzie and Thomas are two of those kids who want to get away before they are taken to military camp. Suzie is fifteen and Thomas is sixteen years old. They both grew up in a very small village with their single mothers. Suzie always wanted to be a poet, and she would always read her poems to her mom. After listening to her daughter's poems, Suzie's mom always said, "Sorry you have to go through this." Thomas was a very hard working kid who would do anything to help and protect his mom. He worked around the clock to support his poor mom, who was losing her sight and getting old. All she knew was that she loved her son dearly, and she believed that she was still alive just to see her son suffer the consequence of war.

One time, Suzie's mom was cleaning her room when she found some poems. She knew they were Suzie's poems, so she told Thomas, who happened to show up looking for her. "Thomas, I am glad you are here. Suzie just left to fetch water from the river, but can you read her poem for me? It's always good to have someone educated," she said, giggling.

All our people in war, peace is what they dream for.
They wonder why blood flows from every door.
They only pray for peace not for their soul.

As Thomas left, her mom imagined what Suzie's life would be if she remained there. She ran to Thomas's mom's house and said to her, "Our kid's lives are in our hands. We have to get them out of this disaster or they will have no future at all." They were both on the same wavelength so they both decided to take their kids away.

"Get up kids, let's go ... it's midnight and no one will see us escape, but you have to be very careful not to say a word or make any noise. You hear me?" said Suzie's mom.

They walked days and nights with no idea of where they were heading. The mothers sang for their kids when they felt that they were safe, and they looked happy, even though they had no food or water, as they walked miles and miles. They enjoyed the sound of birds that replaced the sounds of guns and the screams of the military. They felt that they could smile for the first time in three years, but soon they noticed that they would never be able to make it any further.

They had some food they'd packed, but they gave it to Suzie and Thomas. The mothers never took a bite. They kept on saying, "Dear children, we are old and we are going to die at any moment, but you are too young and brave to die or live the life of misery. All we have to do is to get you out of here, and you will find your own way. It's going to be hard, but nothing in life is easy, do you hear me? Nothing in life is easy."

As they became weaker and weaker, they knew they were going to die soon, so they started giving more and more advice to their kids. "Be strong my children! Do not let anything get in the way of your success and happiness, and no matter what happens to you after this, please promise us that you will never give up!"

"Don't say that Mom. We are still together, and we will be together forever." said Suzie, with tears rolling down her cheeks just like raindrops. As Thomas's Mom lay on the ground powerless, looking up at the mountain, she saw military men standing on the top of it. "There they are, the military. I think they are following us," she said. "Suzie, Thomas, my kids, you have to run," said Suzie's Mom. "No! Not without you," said Thomas.

"Listen to me, dear son; by the time they get here, we will be dead. We are finished! But you, you are the future and you have to make us proud. You have to run and never look back, my kids. Do you hear me?" She took Thomas's hand and said, "Thomas my sunshine, my only hope, promise me that you will take care of my daughter for me. Promise me, my son," she said, as her tears fell. Everyone was crying. It was like a funeral.

"I promise," said Thomas as he looked right into Suzie's eyes and asked, "Do you trust me?"

"Yes," she replied with a shy, fake smile.

"Then run away with me, Suzie. That's what your parents want. They want the best for you, so let's go. Run before they catch us," he said.

As they both looked at their parents, who looked dead, and before the kids could check their heartbeats, they heard a gunshot and ran away, leaving their parents lying on the ground. They ran like there was no tomorrow for several nights and days, still not knowing where they were heading. A million ideas came to mind as they ran and their hearts were bleeding as they pumped faster than ever. They kept blaming themselves for running away without their parents. They weren't even sure if they were dead or alive. The further they ran, the more stressed they became. Even though they were hungry and extremely thirsty, they just didn't feel it until they reached the river.

After three days of walking, they were very happy to finally find some water and some fruit. They were breathless. After they had some fruit and water, Thomas told Suzie a story with a happy ending about a hen and a lion, but when he saw that Suzie was not entertained at all, he asked her to recite her poems for him.

"All my people in the war, peace is what they dream for,
They always wonder why blood flows from every door.
They hear the gun shoot but they don't know where it comes,
They try to escape and follow the route, but each parent dies,
The strong may walk, but the weak can't make it.
Life becomes worthless; how do we could fix it?"

Suzie couldn't continue with her poems anymore, as she was overcome with emotions, washing away tears. Thomas looked at her eyes and wiped her tears.

"I love your poems, but please let's not talk about war anymore," he said. Even though Suzie knew that she would never be able to forget about her parents, her home and the war, she replied, "okay".

Thomas took her hand and said, "It's time to walk again."

As they walked and walked through the bushes, they suddenly reached the main road, but they had no idea where they were. There were very few cars. One showed up every four hours. The first two passed them, even though they tried to stop them. Then a truck came after about an hour.

"Stop... stop... stop," both screamed. "You kids seem lost," said the truck driver, who was carrying marijuana to the border of Uganda. "Please help us get in your truck. We need a ride. We have been walking for weeks and we can't walk any more. Please look at Suzie. She is finished. Please help us," said Thomas in his broken English.

The truck driver, who introduced himself as John, told them to hide under the marijuana so that they would not be caught at the border.

Thomas and Suzie slept in the truck, but the next day the driver woke them up and said, "Alright kids, you are in Uganda, Kampala." They had no idea where that was and had never heard of that country before. Suzie actually thought Uganda was a name of a restaurant or some food place, for she was so hungry. "What is that? I mean what is Uganda?" she asked as she still lay in the truck. "I think that is one of the African countries. I remember learning that in my history class," said Thomas as he stood up from where he was lying.

"You really have no idea? It's just my luck! I had an Ethiopian couple that was running away, but at least they were old enough to take care of themselves. Now what am I going to do with you two? What are your names?" he asked for the first time.

Suzie and Thomas told him every pain and suffering they had gone through, and even though the kids struggled with English, John was very understanding. He took them to his place, where they ate food like animals. He kept them there for two weeks. He treated them like they were his kids, and he loved their company. Suzie, as usual, shared her poems with him, too. John knew that he had to go back to the border again for his job, so he had to find them a job where they would stay and work. Thomas was hired to do a cleaning job so he stayed with John. Suzie got a job as a house girl where she stayed with a single mom with seven children a two-hour drive from where Thomas lived.

For the first week, Suzie felt that the work was too much, but soon she got used to it. She would always cry as she cleaned the house and took care of the kids, but she tried her best to pretend that she was happy. She was homesick, and above all she missed Thomas so much. Thomas missed Suzie a lot, too. He talked about her all the time with John until one day John asked with a smile on his face, "Thomas, you never stop talking about Suzie. Are you in love with this little girl?"

"No," replied Thomas. "Suzie deserves someone way better than me. Besides, this is not time for her or me to ever think about love. I wonder if she ever thinks of me at all," he said looking down. "I wish I was there for her right now. I wish I could just look at her and feel her pain. I am not even there for her as I promised I would be."

John said, "Son, don't worry, you will see everything is going to be alright. All your dreams will come true. You just have to fight to make them happen." Thomas felt like he'd just met his dad who'd died 7 years ago in the war. That piece of advice was worth millions to Thomas.

The next day Thomas went to work, but he had strange feeling that something might have happened to Suzie. He ran home to John's and said, "My heart tells me that Suzie may not be okay. Can we please go see her? It has been three weeks." Off they went.

When Suzie saw Thomas coming, she was so happy that she started laughing and crying at the same time. "I thought I would not see you again," cried Suzie. "I promise I won't let you feel that way again. I am so sorry, Suzie," said Thomas, as he embraced her with his warm hug.

After they talked for a while, Thomas asked, "Suzie, are you going to read me some of your poems? I know you have written a lot down since you had no one to talk to," he said with guilt in his eyes.

"Sure," she replied, "I will go and get the book that John gave me."

My story is so wide,
It hurts deep inside.
It's a painful feeling that I hide
I am helpless, almost tied
For this crime what should I be paid?
For the refugees who have no land,
Why shouldn't we be given some fund?
They are not seen buried underground.

"Suzie," Thomas interrupted, "I love your poems and all that, but you promised that we wouldn't talk about war anymore, remember. We need to move on."

"Ok," said Suzie. "Other poems," she said, as she flipped through the pages. "Let's read together," she said.

I get new feelings slow by slow,
You are stealing my heart, let it grow,
My soul considers you a hero,
I am now happy but worried for tomorrow.
Will you wake me up as I fall?
Cover me from loneliness in your soul,
Protect me from enemies, be my angel.

Suzie looked a little frustrated when Thomas asked her whom she'd written the poems for.

"No one," she replied. Thomas sat closer to her and looked right in her eyes and asked, "Suzie, can we pretend that you wrote this for me?" Suzie didn't say anything, but just stared at him. As Thomas tried to kiss her, a big voice came from behind saying, "Time to go?" Thomas said with the sad voice, "I guess it's time to go."

"Will you come back for me someday?" asked Suzie with tears in her eyes. Thomas took her hand and said, "Suzie, you know how I would love to come for you every second, but I don't really know when I will be back. I promise I will try my best to come back for you as soon as I can. Ok?"

As they left, everyone felt the sadness of a broken heart. Thomas jumped in the truck and waved goodbye to Suzie as she waited for the truck to disappear. Thomas wondered, How will life be for her without loved ones, without peace, living in exile. When will this end? Will I ever be happy? How about dear Suzie? Will I somehow be able to make her happy?

Soon life was better for them. Thomas got a better job and his own place to stay. The family that Suzie worked for moved to the city where Thomas was living, and there they had more time together. Thomas tried every single thing to make Suzie happy, and he was always there for her to dry her tears and kiss her eyes whenever she was unhappy. He protected her just like he promised and never let her down, not even a single day.

This was one of his favorite poems:

Let me be yours please be mine,
Let me kiss you again and take your pain.
Come my love, be with me,
Hug me tight through the night
Set me free and bring me light
When I sit next to you, my heart will have more
When I look in your eyes, my tears won't fall
I have too many reasons to keep you in my soul.

Thomas loved every single moment with her. It had been about a year and half since Suzie had come to the city. He never took her eyes off of her. As they struggled day and night to survive, nothing felt like it was missing in life as long as they had each other. They both loved Africa, but they knew exile is never the right place to settle. Suzie never in her life thought she would be able to spend a day without seeing him. She needed him just like she needed food when she couldn't have it. Suzie learned to have a positive view about life and she learned to say, "Some things are beyond our control, but we have to love what we have."

One day, Suzie got a call from a guy who claimed to be her uncle. Suzie has heard about him and met him only once when she was very young. He lived in Winnipeg, Canada. He said he was willing to sponsor her to Canada. "I would love to come, but not without Thomas. We have gone through hard times together, and I want to get out of here with him," said Suzie.

"Suzie, I am so sorry but I can't sponsor more than one person" said her uncle.

When Thomas heard that Suzie had the opportunity to go to Canada but that she wouldn't go because of him, he said to her, "Suzie, you know you love me and I love you even more, but if you want the best for both of us, you have to take the opportunity, and maybe you can help me." "No! I will never leave you here. I want to die with you, Thomas. Don't you get it? I can't live without you. I will be miserable" she yelled, crying for the first time in a year.

Thomas kissed her tears softly as if it would be the last time and took her hands. "Suzie, remember your mom died for your success. You can't let her down. This is your chance" he said.

In a week, they separated into two different lives. Suzie went to Canada, but Thomas stayed in Africa, surrounded by war and the memories that stuck with him. Two months after Suzie's departure, Thomas decided to travel illegally to Italy in the hopes of meeting with Suzie. He drowned in a lake during his journey. Life for Suzie was never the same. Happiness was something Suzie once had with Thomas, but never after that.

WEYNI ABRAHA grew up on the border of Ethiopia and Eritrea in a small village of about 500 people. When she was 13, she was told that she was old enough to take responsibility for herself and her younger brother. She and her brother left Ethiopia for a safer place. They lived in Uganda where they struggled to learn a new language and a new culture, and where they dealt with extreme homesickness. After many years of struggle, their uncle was able to sponsor them to come to Canada in 2007. Now 19, Weyni is a student at the University of Winnipeg. Her passion includes art and writing stories. She is currently studying international development and hopes to work with the UN or the Red Cross in future.

Next Chapter Please

Alan Balingit

Gazing outside the small porthole of the aircraft, eyes fixed and straining, new life awaits us. Welcoming my family and me is the hazy outline of Winnipeg. That day almost three years ago signifies an end to an old chapter and the beginning of a new one.

After things settle down following the excitement of migrating here, we are confronted with a certain dose of anxiety in anticipation of the future. Facing uncertainties without the comfort of a familiar environment and the support of relatives and friends, trying to start a new life, and moving on in a foreign land is tough. I know that now. Adjusting is not easy. I felt like a fish out of water, wriggling and struggling steadfastly to reach and join the abundant waters of this great nation.

Hundreds of resumes and a couple of interviews later, the first chapter remains unfinished. For sure I am not alone in this situation; most new immigrants face the same dilemma. It is either sink or swim. But what is important is that you know where you want to go. That I know also. I want to pursue my career in the media industry. That is where I want to go in terms of my professional career here. For more than a decade I worked as a journalist, and I dream of regaining that spirit of fulfillment.

But for now, I have a daunting responsibility requiring constant emotional checks, immediate responses, and undying devotion. There are three precious people who came along with me from the Philippines: my wife and two lovely daughters. Winnipeg is giving me an opportunity to learn something new.

Since childhood, the opposite sex had been an enigma to me. They talk, dress, act, and smell differently from us bewildered sons of Adam. Astounding is their capability of abruptly changing disposition from happy to sad, sad to mad, and mad to madder. As a stay-at-home dad, I have come to learn more of their nature than I ever had the chance to discover back home. And I have Winnipeg to thank for that.

"The lure of the distant and the difficult is deceptive. The great opportunity is where you are," John Burroughs once said. That reminds me of one early morning, while I was mopping up after an all-night baking spree at a well-known donut shop where I used to work. When a former co-worker at the store came in for a coffee, he approached me to ask how I was feeling. Tired, unkempt and without sleep, I guess I committed some kind of faux-pas. Good, great, not too bad, or fine was supposed to be the correct response, right? Not knowing what came over me, exhausted, I blurted out frustrated, "I am still here, looking for that bright future."

"You are standing on it buddy, you are standing on it," he said with conviction.

Looking down at the dirty ceramic floor I couldn't see anything bright, other than the product signs hanging above his spaced-out head. With my back aching and hands sore, I finished mopping up the floor, trying to make it cleaner and whiter in time for the influx of customers eager for their morning brew. Looking fresh and recharged, the people seemed to come out of the store with renewed vigor, a hot cup of coffee in hand to start a new day.

Each day brings new challenges and with it hope. My wife often reminds me of this, her soothing encouragement rattles me off my slumber. Things may not always come our way, but when they do, 'seize them', she says. She is right. Our life here hasn't been that easy. Work is as elusive as true friends. I still believe that opportunities are out there, though I haven't found them yet. But for sure when they come, she'll be right there encouraging me to grab them. The hazy outline of Winnipeg may be clearing up; the picture is not yet what we envisioned it would be, but it doesn't matter. The next chapter will be written, and it starts now.

ALAN BALINGIT is a struggling writer trying to make a mark in his new homeland. He has an extensive background working in both the public and private media as an information officer and as a journalist back in his home country of the Philippines. A part time newscaster and writer for the significant Filipino community in Winnipeg, he is a graduate of Business Administration and a product of the tough streets of Manila. He also worked with disadvantaged people as a developmental officer providing livelihood assistance for the poor and the victims of the Mount Pinatubo eruption.

The Philippines is among the most populous countries in the world with 92 million people. It has a diverse culture spread throughout the over 7000 tropical islands. The warm climate attests to the warmth of its people. Perhaps one of the greatest gifts the country gave to the world is the first "People Power Revolution"—a bloodless upheaval that brought down a tyrannical regime. It became the catalyst for future peaceful revolutions in Eastern Europe and other parts of the globe.

You are the Master of Your Life!

Iwona Gniadek

When you live in an English-speaking country, learning English as an Additional (Second) Language does not take place exclusively in the classroom. That is a fact of life. As an adult learner, you must take learning into your own hands and make use of the resources that surround you. Watching TV and movies, listening to the radio, and reading newspapers and magazines are just a few possible ways to improve your skills quickly on your own. In addition, you might consider enrolling in some classes.

"We cannot teach people anything; we can only help them discover it within themselves," said Galileo, the famous philosopher, physicist, and astronomer.

He is right, is he not? Adult learners make conscious decisions about what they want to learn and how they want to learn it. This gives them unlimited power to achieve their goals. Nobody is going to pour English into their heads and find jobs for them. Instead they will be given options and shown opportunities, or simply be exposed to numerous ways to develop their competencies. It is then up to them to pick and choose ways that will help them to achieve their life goals. However, not every immigrant who lands in Canada is self-directed. There is a cultural dimension that plays a major role in a newcomer's autonomy. Some newcomers tend to depend on teachers and counselors to tell them what to do, and how and where to do it. Canadian culture is fairly high on the individualistic scale, which means that although we can be advised, it is we who make the decisions. Canadian culture is also less direct than Asian or Eastern-European cultures, just to name a few. This means that we do not say, "Do it." Instead, we say, "Please feel free to take ownership of the task."

For more information about this, visit (http://www.geert-hofstede.com/) and find out about 'power distance' and individualism in the society of your home country and how it compares to 'power distance' and individualism in Canada. If you come from countries where the power distance index is high, you are likely to follow what you are told without questioning or searching for other sources of information. Therefore, when you land in Canada you might feel lost because nothing appears to be black-and-white.

According to the above-mentioned website, "Canada's Power Distance (PDI) is relatively low, with an index of 39, compared to a world average of 55. This is indicative of a greater equality between societal levels, including government, organizations, and even within families. This orientation reinforces a cooperative interaction across power levels and creates a more stable cultural environment."

Remember that ownership and initiative are the two crucial concepts that apply to all areas of life, be it learning English, searching for information, or typing up a resume.

While some newcomers enjoy the luxury of attending full-time courses, the majority of newcomers are able to attend only part-time classes because they must work to provide for their families. There are still others who cannot attend any classes at all because they work shifts or perhaps hold down more than one job to make ends meet. It doesn't matter what category you belong to; what matters is that you are an adult and you are the master of your life.

I started learning English on my own when I was 12. Of course, I didn't have to learn it because it was not a survival skill that I needed. Rather it was my hobby. Songs, American movies and books were my best friends in my first years of learning. I simply could not get enough of English. Today I am a teacher of English as an Additional Language and a New Canadian. I absolutely love the freedom I have here to own my life and be as self-directed as I wish.

Here are some tips on how to learn English on your own:

- Download podcasts, audio books — whatever material you can find
- Listen to the same recording *over and over again* and repeat after the speakers
- Talk to yourself when you are in front of the mirror. *Imitate* as much as you can and pay attention to how people speak, paying attention to their intonation and pronunciation of words
- Listen to CDs in the car or while doing household chores
- Listen to a variety of accents: American, Canadian, Australian, Indian, British, etc. The more your ears are used to them, the better. You simply never know when being used to all types of English might come in handy
- Again *talk to yourself out loud.*
- Make a list of new words when you read, and immediately use them in conversation.
- Use a monolingual dictionary whenever you can to help you think in English

Remember, first IN, then OUT.

If you want to write well, read voraciously!
If you want to speak well, listen attentively!

On top of letting the language enter your brain, try the following:

- Speak whenever you can, e.g. don't look away when a friendly cashier in a grocery store is trying to make small talk with you and don't ask someone to make that phone call for you.
- Write as much as you can. Buddy up with schoolmates from different cultures, chat on Skype, and exchange e-mails with them outside the classroom.

Are you one of those people who think they are too old to learn a language? You are wrong. It takes a positive attitude, and nothing else. If you can develop strategies to learn a foreign language and use them, you can learn any language, no matter what age you are. You can learn a language as easily as you can learn how to drive, how to handle a till, etc.

Where there's a will, there's a way!

Your ultimate goal should be self-sufficiency. Unless you start now, it will be hard to achieve your goals fast. Don't wait for people to teach you things or tell you what to do. The Internet is full of English learning resources that you can have fun with in the quiet of your own home at your own convenience. If you don't know where to look, ask your teacher. Your teacher will be happy to guide you because that is his role. What's more, impress your teacher with how self-directed you are and help your fellow learners to become more self-directed.

I promise you: soon English will become an integral part of you, just like your first language.

Go on, have fun indulging in English!

Nobody can say that **IWONA GNIADEK** hasn't traveled. Born in Poland, she visited New York, USA, and experienced life and work in London, England, before finally arriving in Canada. She has now established herself as an English Language teacher for newcomers to the country and holds an M.A. in the subject from the University of Warsaw. Although she has been in Canada for over three years, she still considers herself a newcomer but as traveling and languages are in her blood she embraces each new day with a passion. Canada crossed her life agenda when, at the age of fourteen, she watched the Olympic Games in Calgary. 'Dreams come true if we really want them to,' says Iwona. 'Where there's a will, there's a way' is her life motto.

Poland, her home country, is an ancient nation conceived in the middle of the tenth century. It lies in Central Europe and is bordered by the Baltic Sea,

Germany, The Czech Republic, Slovakia, The Ukraine, Lithuania, Belarus and Russia. The country is 32 times smaller than Canada but has a bigger population of 38 million. Just like Canada, it has it all: the lakes and the sea, the high mountains and prairies. It also has a desert.

Myeongsook's Poem

Myeongsook Jung

I am standing at the Millennium Library bus stop.
A big yellow bus is coming.
A big wind is following.
Pursuing the wind,
Fallen leaves are spinning and spinning like me.

I am a three-and-a-half month newcomer.
Chasing a newcomer's dream,
I am spinning and spinning in downtown Winnipeg, like the
    leaves.
The ESL morning class at 11 Promenade. There I am.
The afternoon class at 297 Portage Avenue. There I am.
The weekend computer class at 167 Lombard Avenue. There I
    am, too.
And then,
I am standing at the Millennium Library bus stop, again.

The leaves are still there.
They are whispering to me like a witch.
You are a baby here.
No matter how hard you chase your dream,
You are still a baby.
You can't imagine how tough it is and will be.
You shall be stranded in the coming harsh winter.

The baby responds to her.
No way.
You don't understand me.
You cannot imagine how strong I am.
I am not like you.

How stupid you are to be still there.

You will be stagnant like stationary water.
I am not like you.
I am streaming with the dream.

No matter what obstacles I face
I will cross them,
And jump them,
So I am not like you.
Because I am not stagnant forever.

MYEONGSOOK JUNG was born in Seoul. She has BA in journalism from the Hankuk University of Foreign Studies in Korea. She has worked for the Discovery Channel as a subtitle translator. The job was perfectly suited for her because she is really enthusiastic about toying with words and metaphors. What she murmurs every day is 'If the tide of change approaches, your loyalty will be rewarded.' For her, the motto is a beacon of 'dreams coming true'. That is why she is spinning her wheels downtown in Winnipeg every single day.

Her mother country, Korea is located between China and Japan. Such a geographical environment has resulted in sharing common traits with its neighbors in many aspects. Nevertheless, it has developed its own rich and indigenous culture and arts. The 13th Century explorer, Marco Polo depicted Korea as the "Land of the Morning Calm", which has tranquil beauty. These days, the ice queen Kim Yu-na, the UN Secretary-General Ban Ki-moon, world-class companies Samsung and Hyundae are other names that stand for developed and vibrant Korea.

Jill Lin's Story

Jill Lin

Eighteen years ago, there was a girl born in Taipei, Taiwan, one of the most crowded cities in the world. Now, this girl is sitting in front of a desk, writing her story. Who is she? You must wonder. Actually, I am that girl. And this is my story.

My full name is Fang-Ju Lin, but my nickname is Jill. I was born in Taiwan-Formosa, an incredible island with friendly people. I come from a traditional Taiwanese family. My father is a music teacher and composer, my mother is a housekeeper, and my younger brother is a university student. We also have Mimi, our lovely cat, who joined our family seven years ago.

I have been passionate about art since I was a child. When I was three years old, my father started teaching me the piano because he expected I would become a musician like him. During my childhood, he gave me strict training and used many creative ways to inspire my interest in piano. For example, he trained me to hold an egg in the palm of my hand while playing the piano. However, my passion for music was not as great as my passion for painting. In elementary school, I entered various drawing competitions, with good results. Thus, my parents sent me to art school, and I started learning to draw. My passion for painting motivated me to choose art and design as my career. Eventually, I became a graphic designer after graduating from university.

Exploring the world is one of my favourite pastimes. I have enjoyed many unforgettable experiences on many journeys, from meeting different people, to experiencing different cultures, to visiting impressive sights. I have visited Japan, China, Italy, Canada and the U.S. This year, I stayed in Tokyo for two months with my fiancé. We climbed Fuji Mountain on a very windy and rainy day. I still remember the cold wind like a sword stabbing into my bones. Because of the lack of oxygen, we developed headaches and became dizzy. However, in spite of this, we now can say that we have stood on the top of the tallest mountain in Japan. During these trips, I deeply felt that traveling is a significant way to enrich my life and broaden my horizons.

The one thing I spend most of my time doing is meditating. I enjoy creative thinking, the process that inspires my mind to create such things as a new graphic design. People think that graphic design is just a pattern limited to the visual sense. In my view, graphic design is a reflection of psychology and social norms. For example, different hues give people different feelings. A successful advertising campaign comes from a person's needs in society. Needless to say, I spend a lot time implementing new ideas.

This is my story. Today, I am living in Winnipeg, Canada, one of the coldest cities on the earth. The girl from Taipei is now starting another journey here in Canada.

 JILL LIN is a graphic designer and an artist from Taipei, Taiwan. She has a B.A in Commercial Design from the University of Ming-Chang in Taiwan. She is enthusiastic in creating unique design styles and paintings. Currently, she has ambitions to found a design studio with her husband in Winnipeg.

Taiwan, also known as Formosa, is a beautiful island off the coast of south-eastern China. Taiwan is a melting pot of various cultures, both Chinese and foreign, with aboriginal cultures mixed in, thus creating a unique socio-cultural flavor. Taiwan is famous for its delicious food, exciting nightlife, and friendly people. When it comes to eating, Taiwan is a gourmet's paradise. The (now second) tallest building in the world — Taipei 101 — is located in the capital city of Taipei, complete with world-class restaurants, a shopping mall and movie theatres.

From +40 C to −40 C: Why I Want to Write

Deepa Narula

My thoughts go back to our first winter in Winnipeg. January is not the best time to arrive in Winnipeg, but that's when I arrived with my ten-year-old and one-and-a-half-year-old sons in tow. Every time I discussed our family's settling-down woes with my children's day care director, she would exclaim, "From +40 to −40 degrees Celsius, what an absolute changeover for the little ones!" After being a Delhiite for thirty-three years to becoming a year old Winnipegger, time and again I find my thoughts oscillating between there and here, then and now. Recalling the hardships of our first winter in Winnipeg, I am filled with apprehension at the prospect of the approaching subzero months. It leads me to reminisce about the excitement the beginning of October generated when I lived in Delhi. As the temperatures cooled down, a palpable excitement filled the air as we anticipated the spate of festivals, weddings, celebrations and parties that would commence from October onwards and continue till March.

I remember the first time my husband had broached the idea of applying for immigration to Canada; like me he too had to go to the wall very often, trying to get things moving or getting people to change their attitudes. In the school where I taught for ten years, I had gained notoriety for my "absurd and impractical" ideas. It had become a boring pattern. I would approach the principal on some issue, only to beat a hasty retreat. I was an upstart trying to challenge convention and the status quo, so I would be routed. Even requests for more fans in the classroom of forty-five adolescents (where there were only two overhead fans circulating the stale and hot air) would draw responses like "toughen them up," "we don't want to spoil them in luxury," and so on! Whether it was a request for an earlier lunch break and recess for the children in the lower primary classes or a plea to reduce the stress of examinations or syllabi to cram for, it would all be turned down on the same grounds.

My confrontations with the parents of the students I taught were sometimes worse. Once I tried to convince the parents of a diligent student who loved literature and wanted to study it at the university to let him study the subjects of his choice. But my pleas fell on deaf ears. The parents wanted to see their vicarious ambitions of becoming a doctor fulfilled through their son. They forced him to study medical sciences, but he failed in the science exams. Unable to bear the shame and disappointment, he was sure his parents would feel, he hanged himself from the ceiling fan of his home.

Since I have "subbed" in various schools through the past year, I have become an enthusiast for the education pattern in Canada. I admire the practical approach and the student-centered teaching methodology that encourages self-directed learning. I am impressed with the huge wealth of children's literature available here. In India, I was dissatisfied with both the education curriculum and methodology. The state of science education may be a little better, but the condition of humanities and arts education is languishing. Most universities do not have the system of term papers or assignments to check a student's work through the year. Throughout my studies I was never asked to write a paper apart from taking end-of-term exams.

As an entrepreneur in India, my husband had a lot of ideas that he wanted to develop. All his plans remained plans and never came close to materializing because everything revolved around nepotism and bribing somebody to get anything moving at all. So together we made the decision to immigrate to Canada. It was a good four years before our immigration came through. When our passports arrived with the coveted "Immigrant Visa" stamped on them, we were ecstatic. My husband stressed the need to carefully stow our passports, "Our passports are now worth lots of rupees … always remember how much people are ready to pay to get out of this country." It is true. The glamour of non-resident East Indians arriving with their cologne-bathed suitcases, shiny bags of cosmetics and photographs showing the pride of possession of their show homes and SUV's has certainly turned thousands into aspiring Canadian immigrants. When we drive through Punjab, we can see miniature airplanes with the Air Canada logo on roof-tops. Every other family has relatives in Canada, and the success stories of visiting immigrants certainly lure the ones behind to jump on the bandwagon and apply for Canadian immigration. We too gained the envy of our Punjabi cousins who were trying their utmost to get a Canadian visa. So as soon as our visas arrived, we got ready to try our fortune in this Great White North.

Friends had counseled us against traveling to Canada during the winter, especially because my younger child was only a year and half old. But we threw all caution to the wind. We were actually excited to arrive in the holiday season. As Delhiites, our cherished winter break was to holiday in the snow-covered hills of Mussoorie or Manali. One of my fondest holiday memories is of playing with snowballs as a child when our family holidayed in Shimla during the winter break. The other time was when I was on my honeymoon in the hills of the Himalayas and found my wishes come true, as it had unexpectedly snowed in early December. Back in Delhi, we create make believe snow out of cotton wool for the Christmas and New Year's decorations. The world has shrunk into a global village, which is what explains the snowmen and plastic Christmas trees even though there is no snow and no pine trees in Delhi. We were eager to see the excitement of the holiday season in Canada and get to feel the real snow. We landed in Toronto and enjoyed the Christmas and New Year's parties. That was our brief holiday and interlude before we arrived in Winnipeg and got down to the business of putting down roots in Canada.

My love for the cold weather certainly took a beating as I was forced to face the subzero temperatures and wind chill of January in Winnipeg. Even the winter coats we had bought on arriving seemed ineffectual against the freezing cold as I waited at or walked to and from bus stops. I was stricken speechless when my sister in Delhi (whom I'd called up and told about the snowstorms) said, "Lucky you, you must be enjoying the snow!" We spent the entire month shopping for home supplies and settling down in Winnipeg. Since we had been in such a rush to come over to Canada, we had not even considered disposing off our assets back in India. So during early February my husband had to go back. It would be several months before he could safely wind down and sell the properties. That meant that I would have to be on my own, taking care of the children in a new city. As the day of his departure approached, we realized that I had to get a driver's license. I was a little apprehensive about how quickly I would get accustomed to driving here, even though everybody said, "If you can drive in Delhi, you can drive anywhere." I took a few driving lessons, but I was utterly flabbergasted by the enormity of the difference between driving in Delhi and in Winnipeg. My usually affectionate husband became an infuriated and short-tempered instructor as he gave me last minute driving lessons; he could not understand why I did not quickly adapt to driving in Canada, unlike him. I ascribed his quickness to the fact that he had driven in the U.S as a teenager. Both of us were filled with enormous foreboding. I was in a new city, without close friends or family, and I had the formidable task of safely transporting the children to and from school and daycare everyday. If I did not pass the driving test before the scheduled date of his departure, visions of pushing my son in the stroller for a fifteen-minute walk from Pembina Highway to his daycare gave me shivers. Delhi's traffic is modeled upon the British pattern, so it's left side drive and left turns are free. The fact that I was starting to drive in Winnipeg when there were three-foot high snow-banks and icy roads did not help either. I took the test under duress and quite predictably failed (three times) because I had stopped for pedestrians or children near the road. Fortunately, the fact that I had driving experience of over ten years in Delhi counted, and I was allowed to repeat the test several times during that month. Finally, a day before my husband's departure, I passed the test.

As my husband was leaving to take the flight to Delhi, we were both filled with misgivings because of the enormity of the responsibility that rested on me. He repeatedly entreated me to drive carefully for the children's sake. After he left, my mornings became especially nerve wracking because I had started working as a substitute teacher. It meant I would get called in the morning about which school I had to go that day, and I was unfamiliar with the location of practically all the schools in the division. Between packing our lunches, getting ready for school and going over Map Quest for directions to get to the school where I was working, I was a mass of jitters. The first day after my husband left for Delhi and I was driving to school, I had just changed lanes to move with the flow of traffic when I got rear-ended! I had no time to soothe the shaken and crying baby in the backseat while I hastily exchanged information with the other car's driver. My husband had not even landed in India and I had managed to have an accident. Even though the other driver accepted responsibility because of momentary inattention and the icy road, the accident reduced me to a bundle of shaking and quaking nerves every morning after that.

As a new Canadian, I find myself constantly thinking about what I would be doing now if I were in Delhi. My mind is drawing up an inventory of sorts, reflecting on what I have lost and gained since I immigrated to Canada. I certainly miss the joy and closeness of family and festivals, but what I have gained is much more. What I think I have gained is a new perspective. Among many immigrants I have noticed (especially the ones that do not frequently travel to India) the tendency to romanticize their imaginary Indias. They gloss over and sometimes even forget the problems that drove them to seek immigration. Before my perception becomes clouded by nostalgia, I want to record this double perspective of a migrant. I want to remember how each of my favorite things became flawed. In India, I was an avid reader of literature and worshipped it for giving me access to many different worlds. In Canada, I have discovered opportunities to help me write and maybe share my stories with both fellow Winnipeggers and Delhiites.

 **DEEPA NARULA** I immigrated from New Delhi, India and settled with my husband and two children in Winnipeg in 2006. I had won a Doctoral Research Fellowship for research at the University of Manitoba for my PHD in Canadian Aboriginal literature. In my thesis I examine Aboriginal literature as a "real" Indian writing about the literature of the mistaken "Indians" and I hope to remove stereotypes and develop understanding about the Aboriginal people among the East Indian communities in Winnipeg as well as India. I work as substitute teacher in several school divisions in Winnipeg and also as freelance writer for "The Indo-Canadian Telegram", the East Indian community newspaper. I also help in my husband's retail business that specializes in Pashmina scarves, Indian handicrafts, home decor and musical instruments. As a newcomer who successfully integrated into the workforce, my profile is live at this Manitoba Labor and Immigration website and the link is:

http://www.immigrantsandcareers.mb.ca/cdmbnewcomers/171_180/173_deepa_n/basic_facts/

Home, A Place for Sharing

Florence Okwudili

The rooster crowed at 4:00 a.m., alerting humans to prepare to wake up. It crowed again at 4:30 a.m., then at 5:30 a.m., this time joined by other sleepy roosters, who had for some reason forgotten their jobs. At 5:30 a.m., other birds joined the rooster in an excitement of singing, ushering in a new day.

Obi turned lazily in his bed, wishing to sleep some more.

"I hope that someday Grandma will sell this rooster," he said to himself. He wished morning would never come.

The rooster stopped crowing at 5:30 a.m. and was up and about his duty, looking for food. Later, Obi woke up and joined the already busy environment full of activities started by other creatures. For some, it's time to go to bed; for others it is "Hoooraaay!! What a new day." Obi stretched his arms, yawning, wishing the birds would stop singing and fly away, never to come back to their nest resting on the big Iroko tree facing Obi's house.

"Chirp!! Chirp!! Chirp!!" sang three little baby chicks, as they raised their voices in a harmonious song of agitation. "Oh! No!" cried the mother bird, which had just flown away in search of food for her chicks. "Something must be wrong with my babies; I must get back to them immediately!" Flapping her wings and in a louder and stronger "Chirp! Chirp! Chirp!" the mother bird flew back to the nest securely fitted in between two branches, and soon the baby chicks were calm.

Obi gradually awakened to the songs of other species of birds, the morning sunshine, and the gentle wind that blows the trees so that they sway in unison to the command of the wind, making a whistling sound and joining the millions of other animals living and sharing the same space in the joy of having a new day.

The mouse ran very fast past Obi, into a hole and up into the ceiling.

"Warm and cozy, away from the humans and away from daylight," he thought to himself. "Here, I can wait, listen and watch," said the mouse to himself. "It's a matter of time and everything will be quiet again."

"Buzzzzz! Buzzing! Buzzzzzzz!" the fly flew around in a delightful frenzy over the plate of leftover food. "These humans sure do have delicious food. I think I have found a home at last: up in the air and out of reach of humans."

The ants slowly made their way back into their holes away from sight.

"I wish we could go further into the daylight and into the field." "But we must hide. Otherwise, our lives will be stomped out."

Wait a minute, I almost forgot, said Obi to himself. I need to take the sheep out for grazing before the sun becomes too strong. Obi ran into the shed, untied the seemingly anxious sheep and led them out of the compound to the farmland for grazing.

"Obi! Obi!" Grandmother Sarah called from the back side of the building. "Remember to put fresh water out for the goats before having your breakfast."

"Yes Mama," replied Obi.

After finishing his morning chores, Obi got ready for school. Settling down to have his breakfast, he wondered what the world would be like without these other creatures that share our world.

Grandmother Sarah always said that animals deserved the same treatment as humans because we share our home with other creatures, which must also live and share the earth with us.

FLORENCE NGOZI OKWUDILI was born in Port-Harcourt, Nigeria, shortly before the Nigerian Civil war erupted. Her parents fled Port-Harcourt and took refuge in a village while the war lasted for four years. After the war, her parents moved back to the city of Lagos where they continued life, but with occasional visits to the village.

Although she grew up for the most part in the cities of Nigeria, except for with the annual visits to the village, her inspiration in life has always come from the experiences of the village visits. The striking differences that exist between life in the city and life in the village never cease to amaze her. She incorporates her love of village life in her children's stories.

The Significance of Human Diversity to the World

Nathaniel Ondiaka

It was September, 2007, that the writing group for new immigrants was born. Under the patronage of the Millennium Library, people from Kenya, Ethiopia, India, Philippines, Macedonia, Korea, and other parts of the world came together to pursue their common love for writing in our adopted homeland, Canada.

The small room on the second floor of the library in downtown Winnipeg aptly dotted with murals of cultural diversity and harmony became the meeting place for the group.

Despite coming from different cultural, societal, and religious backgrounds, the group integrated and shaped a unique blend of kinship, whose perceptions, judgments and understanding of the word "global" transcends borders. The pains, joys, and dreams of each one of us were manifested through our written words.

Our writing has enabled us to share and appreciate diverse cultures and traditions. It has created a clearer picture of each other's background, which has altered the preconceived notions that are usually borne of ignorance; it has facilitated a greater respect and understanding of each other.

The experience has also made me learn to appreciate my own cultural identity. I am Kenyan by birth, adopted by a Japanese man. I studied in China and married a Chinese woman with whom I have two kids. I now live in Canada. My persona is fashioned by my familiarity with people of these great nations and their diverse cultures.

I was born 46 years ago in Nakuru, a city in the world-famous Great Rift Valley, a natural marvel of the world that can be seen from the moon! Kenya is made up of 42 tribes, each with a distinctive language and cultural practices. The nature of my father's occupation enabled my siblings and me to traverse the entire country, exposing us to people of different cultures, social-economic backgrounds and ethnic affiliations.

Mastery of local language(s), acceptance, and appreciation of neighborhood cultures ensured that initially annoying, scary and hurting moments turned into enrichment and affirmation of our new neighborhoods. These values prepared us adequately for our future challenges and careers in various fields of academia in places as far away as Britain, China, Poland, Israel, Holland and South Africa.

Our desire to surmount cultural diversities paid off handsomely. Our family is now endowed with professionals in various scholarly disciplines. My brother, a Poland-trained architect, has recently settled in Toronto. One of my sisters, an agricultural engineer, works for an international organization based in Nairobi. My kid sister is currently pursuing her PhD in Biochemistry in Holland, while I am a medical doctor and surgeon living in Canada.

I first left Kenya on a study scholarship provided by the government of the People's Republic of China through the Ministry of Education in my home country. I proceeded to China in 1986, where I spent a total of nine and half years. There I studied Chinese Mandarin, a prerequisite to medicine courses, as well as Traditional Chinese Medicine, graduating in July 1994 with a Bachelor's degree in Medicine and a Bachelor's degree in Surgery.

Upon graduation, and still on a Chinese Government grant, I took an additional year of specialized training in General Surgery. During this period, I had the opportunity of serving the Chinese people in my capacity as a trainee surgeon in one local hospital in the southern city of Canton.

China is composed of 56 different tribes and cultures, 96% Han nationality. Initially, communication barriers curtailed critical thinking that led to negative perceptions and judgment of events bordering on prejudice. There was the CAB mentality with Caucasians at the top, Asians in the middle and Blacks at the bottom, a clear racial classification.

Cultural awareness, pre-conception and coalition building helped bridge these cultural gaps. The fact that I survived China for close to a decade leads me to conclude that I can survive anywhere, despite any hardships or challenges. My efforts to win over my Chinese classmate, my "better half," rubbed a few Chinese men the wrong way.

Her family, as well as mine, from the same generation with mindsets focused on preserving local cultures, were rattled and could not envisage their loved one plunging into the murky waters of marrying a foreigner. Our marriage in China was approved by neither her parents nor mine, who were vehemently opposed to the relationship from the start.

We started our life on a sour note and had to work hard to bring together the two families. Their initial misgivings about our relationship were eventually cleared up and the two families are now friends.

Looking back, I am happy to have been one of Kenya's pioneers in China. Apart from qualifying as a physician, I met an elderly Japanese man who was childless and grieving the loss of his wife to breast cancer. He would later adopt me as his son. He is 80 years old.

I also witnessed two major historical events towards the end of the last century: the coming to an end of the Cold War with the fall of the Berlin Wall in 1989, and the transformation of China into an open society and its integration into the family of nations.

Upon graduation, my wife and I returned to Kenya to start a new life. As a young interracial and unemployed couple, this was not easy either. After close to a decade of absence, a lot seemed totally foreign to me.

Interracial marriages are common in Kenya, though marriage to a Chinese national is uncommon. Due to her race, many people in Kenya thought I was "her servant"; most probably her driver. This reverse psychology applied whenever we visited China, and I would likewise be accorded royal treatment.

Some years after we settled in Kenya, we relocated to Canada in October, 2004. We were preceded by my cousin, who arrived here in 2003 to undertake a piloting course at Gimli. Upon his return to Kenya, he had very kind words about Canada in general and Gimli and Winnipeg, in particular. This motivated my family to move to Canada.

On arrival here, the people I encountered stirred me. It seemed like I was strolling the entire globe; I comfortably conversed with different people in Swahili, English, Mandarin and Cantonese. It was such an awesome introduction to Canada.

I also had the opportunity to have a chat with one of Canada's icons, Gerry W. Schwartz, the CEO of Onex Corporation. He addressed me in such a respectful manner that it left me feeling welcome here. Mr. Schwartz even bought me a piece of pizza. In my country of birth, such an important person is unapproachable and usually surrounded by mean-looking bodyguards armed to the teeth.

Lest we forget, migrants from across the world have relocated and established homes all over Canada, a country once unanimously voted by the United Nations as the "best country" for immigrants. Commonly referred to as "visible minorities", they make a significant representation in Canada, just about 16% of Canada's population of 33.2 million. This without doubt has fashioned a near perfect "*step out of one's cultural box*" human race. Similar trends are replicated in other nations that have embraced and nurtured a multiplicity of cultures engendering the "Global Village" phenomenon.

Nevertheless, with diversity comes adversity. Because of language barriers, new immigrants encounter problems accessing essential services, credit records and photo IDs, making the first few months dreadful.

Some traditional Canadians tend to perceive immigrants as refugees, generously supported by the Canadian government. Assimilation of new migrant professionals into the Canadian workforce is not as smooth on account of their lack of Canadian experience and the failure of the licensing bodies to acknowledge and/or recognize foreign attained credentials. This situation is driving new immigrants to seek refuge and help from their ethnic communities, negating the very essence of multiculturalism and diversity. The city of Winnipeg is now being systemically partitioned into ethnic cocoons: St. Boniface—French, Maples—Filipino, China town—Chinese.

My view on the much-touted initiative, the "Global Village", other than the realisation of ease of communication through technological advances, is that it has not done much for the integration of people from different ethnic backgrounds. This has given rise to people from the same cultures and backgrounds isolating themselves from the rest and setting up territorial boundaries within major cities of the world as opposed to integrating into society.

I lost both my biological parents while abroad: my mother while I was a student in China, and my father a year after I relocated to Canada with my family as permanent residents in October 2004.

Am I Kenyan? Or am I Chinese? Or am I Japanese? I am all rolled into one—I am international.

 NATHANIEL CHIMASIA ONDIAKA was born in Kenya (East Africa), studied and graduated in the People's Republic of China, practiced medicine, both conventional and traditional, in Guangzhou (Canton), China and Kenya as well. He is fluent in several languages including Luhya, Swahili, English, Mandarin, Cantonese, French and Japanese. He married Liwen Zhang upon graduating from a medical school in southern China. They have two children, both attending Winnipeg schools. He and the family immigrated to Canada in October 2004 as permanent residents. He is the president of the Kenyan Association of Manitoba, and works with the Winnipeg Regional Health Authority in addition to acting as a consultant.

Kenya is one of the most beautiful countries south of the Sahara endowed with natural wonders and animal species of many kinds. The Great Rift Valley and the 0 degree Equator cross each other in Kenya. This is the place to visit on your next honeymoon. The people there are very welcoming just as Winnipeggers are friendly.

Home

Daniela Ristova

The first thing that comes to mind when I think about home is the place that I feel attached to at the moment. It can be the parent's home, a dormitory, an apartment, or a house that you rent. There are also homes that you live in for years, where you don't feel you belong, and you can't wait to get out of. I believe one of the most powerful feelings that makes you feel at home is a sense of belonging.

Home is more than the place where you live. Home can be in your dreams or your plans; home can be in your memories—places where you have lived. It can be in your imagination, like a perfect home where there is peace, wisdom, understanding, laughter and love. There are some disciplines and rules too, so that it can be harmonious. It's a place where you feel comfortable and safe, where you can close the door and leave all of the problems out.

Once you've had a home, everything else that's any different looks false. And you search to find that home in other places. Sometimes the materialistic side of the belonging can cause the psychological feeling of belonging, so it's a big event for some people to start to feel at home somewhere. I have never owned a house to know that part of belonging, but I know the feeling of belonging even if it's not in my own house, just knowing that people accept me as I am. I have good memories from most places that I have lived in and people that I have lived with.

I will never forget my first home. It was with my grandmother and I am so happy about it, because it gave me a good example of what a real home can be. It represented peace, understanding, wisdom, laughter and love. It gave me freedom to be me and to do what I wanted while still respecting some rules. It was at that home where Santa came to bring me gifts. It was a home where I believed in miracles. If someone had asked me then about finding another home elsewhere, I would never have left there. I am still looking for that home. I hope that I will be able to buy a little house with a big yard where my son can play. He will have good memories when he grows up of what a real home can be.

There is scientific information that cats are attached more to the places they live in and dogs are more attached to the people they live with. I think it is similar with people. Some people tend to be attached to the place and the tradition and never leave, but they dream to travel and see the world. Some people take their family and see the world and live in different cultures, but they miss their friends, family and traditions from their home country.

In my country, in the last 15 years it has become difficult to create warm harmonious homes. Because of the bad economy, most couples can't afford to buy their own houses so they have to live with their parents even after they are married and have children. The cultural and age differences between parents and children can cause conflicts in the home for all of them. That's one of the reasons young couples are trying to find homes in other countries, and it's one of the reasons we came to Canada. It is hard to leave your home country and your home, where everything is familiar and comfortable, and go somewhere else, facing the fear of the unknown, to start from the beginning and learn everything again like a small child.

I miss my family and my friends a lot and will do everything to visit them as often as possible, but I don't regret that I came because my home is the entire world. I can go and adapt to living anywhere as long as there is peace, justice and basic needs. The world is full of beautiful places and friendly people, and it is now my home.

DANIELA RISTOVA was born in Munich, Germany, but grew up in a small town in Macedonia. The best part of her childhood was the time spent with her grandmother in a mountainous village in eastern Macedonia. Being a teenager during the transition of Macedonia from communism to democracy, she chose to study Economics as it was one of the most popular post secondary education fields at that time with better chance of getting a job.

Witnessing that transition as well as the independence of Macedonia from Yugoslavia meant experiencing the economic crisis in the country and difficulty in finding employment. That was one of the reasons why she went for summer work in England and then immigrated to Canada. She came 5 years ago and step by step went through another transition called cultural shock or settling, starting with learning the language, looking for a job, making friends and becoming a Canadian citizen. Going through many transitions she decided she liked changes and that's how she found the Writing Group for New Canadians, looking for ways to improve her English skills.

Home

Zulfiya Tursunova

What is home? Such a hard question to answer. What comes to my mind first is that home is the house, apartment, or room where I live alone or with family members.

But how many people in this world have a place to live? How many people in Canada, USA, Europe and the rest of the world sleep in cardboard boxes or under the sky, without a roof over them? How could we allow this to happen? Allow children, women, men, and elders to live in misery, without food, care, and love? What has happened to us? We allow governments to send troops abroad, to spend money on arms production, and let people die? Why?

Home is the place where I live, the place where I sleep, eat, and share my sorrow and joy. Home is the place where I can rush to after school, work, or after having a walk outside. Home is my protector from the sun, wind, rain and snow. Home is the place where I tell stories: stories of what happened to me today, stories about my family, ancestors, land, nature and our being.

Let us ensure that everyone has a home.

Home is the place where I was born. It is where my "place-ness", identity and belonging came into play. It is a place where I remember each tree, flower, pavement, where I remember the singing of birds. My family moved into the center of the city of Tashkent in Uzbekistan. I cannot imagine that I could be born in other parts of the city like my elder brother and sister. I recall my neighbours with whom I would play peacefully and quarrel with if they offended my brothers and sisters.

I loved the community swimming pool, which we would clean, fill with water, and swim in. I loved it so much, especially in summer when it was so hot. I would spend many hours swimming and lying on the edge of the swimming pool, talking to myself and dreaming. Sometimes, when it became late, my neighbour, Aunt Nadya, would call me and say, "Zulfiya, it is becoming late. Probably you have had enough swimming for today. Don't you want to go home?" I would listen to her wise advice and would go home. Aunt Nadya was a very kind person. She lived on the first floor. Sometimes when we children played in the yard and became thirsty, we would call Aunt Nadya and ask her for water. She would bring us water. We would thank her and continue our playing.

Let us ensure that each child has a good neighborhood with trees, a place to play and good and kind neighbours.

Home is my city, which tells me a story through monuments, buildings, roads, museums, parks, plants and factories. It speaks to me through the architecture, pictures, and signs. Home is my soul, "soul at peace," which can rest and rely on others in case of hardships, difficulties, sorrow and grief.

Home is the place I travel to work, study or visit. It is a very enriching experience. It is an experience of connection, connection to people similar to me who shared and still share the same colonial history.

My experience in Canada has been eye-opening in terms of learning of what has been done to native people. My soul is with them, as it is an experience that can connect people, and thus create a shared meaning. It is a difficult journey native people around the world are taking to restore justice. It is our journey, our vocation, our self-determination of our true home.

The poem about the reed flute written by Rumi calls for finding home because the flute's home was the reed it was cut from to make the flute. Rumi's poem also calls for the 'past that exists in the future,' where time and meaning is in harmony. This poem advocates for the meaningful relations with other people and a universe where time and the pace of life are grounded in the quality of human relations. My flute is Uzbekistan. No matter where I live for work or study, my home is where my soul was born. The older I become, the stronger the flute calls me back ... my home is my "soul at peace," and that is where I belong.

Let us ensure that that everyone has a home.

ZULFIYA TURSUNOVA

Spring Will Happen

Rossana Velasco

When I first arrived in Canada, it was like setting foot on a wide, empty space. Don't get me wrong. Canada is a well-developed country with rich resources, but being an immigrant, I felt that to live here was to begin with nothing and to explore everything.

My first encounter with the cold was something I could never have imagined. I didn't know what was more dominant: the coldness biting into my skin or the coldness from being far from familiar people and being nowhere near the place that I knew as well as my own name. It was the night of February 4, 2006. My relatives welcomed my father and me, saying that we were lucky to arrive on a night when the temperature was so mild. Mild? I could not imagine how it could be even colder than it was. My ears and fingers were feeling a certain biting pain for the first time.

During my first few days around Winnipeg, I was like a kid afraid of my new surroundings. I had to be careful with every action, every decision and every encounter with people. I had to watch my movements; it was like being inside a store that sells fragile, expensive items. One wrong move and I could break something. It was almost like learning again the things that I should already know. I had to learn how to dress properly to be bundled up against the cold. I can't count how many times my aunt stopped me at the door saying that I had to go back and change because what I was wearing was not suited for the temperature outside. I needed to learn how to work the balance between the cold and hot water faucets. Back in my home country, we could only get hot water by boiling water in a kettle. Then there were the bus stops that I had to remember and the bus schedules that I needed to adhere to, or else I'd be standing in the cold for the next 20 minutes waiting for the next bus.

The first ever appointment I had here in Canada was in the doctor's clinic. I needed medication for my swollen toe on my right foot. The shoes I was wearing during the long trip from the Philippines were not that comfortable. I really did not want to go, but my aunt insisted. Maybe it was because I could not hide the pain in my face every time I stepped on my right foot. So I got my first ever prescription, which was an antibiotic. During that time, I wished too, that there were prescriptions to cure my homesickness.

The swollen toe continued for a few more weeks. For a period of time, I thought the antibiotics weren't doing the job. This could not be how Canada welcomed me. I had to wear my right shoe improperly, with the back flap folded down so I could step on it. My ankles were exposed so my swollen toe would have more room inside the shoe.

But that did not stop me from exploring Winnipeg.

I went with my aunty wherever she needed to go. Although limping with my right leg, I went out to experience all my other "firsts" here in Canada. I attended a funeral viewing; I joined my aunt and other elderly ladies for a dinner night out; I got my first sip of Tim Horton's coffee, and my first gulp of Canadian liquor too. I was invited to several house gatherings. And the most common thing that people at every occasion wanted to know was why I was wearing my shoe that way. I can't remember how many times I had to explain the reason.

Although I could not imagine how I could work with such a bad toe, I immediately applied for jobs. The first set of resumes I sent out were for jobs relating to my field. After a month of silence, I stopped sending out such resumes. I started applying for any jobs I thought I could handle, even without related experience. I applied as a production worker, call center agent, waitress and housekeeper. One time I got rejected after applying for a cashier's position when the boss reasoned that since I was new to Canada, I did not know what each bill looked like. So after that, there followed many mornings when I woke up with the scary realization that I was still jobless. I thought "Where else can I go?" My education was not granted accreditation, and it was impossible to gain experience in other fields because no one would hire me.

So each day went on with me waiting for calls. They were the same: one cold day after another, as I lived with the daily routine of searching for new job posts, handing in resumes personally and cleaning my swollen toe with antiseptic during intervals. Sometimes when the snow was falling, I'd sit by the window and watch as the snowflakes fell from the sky. They were gracefully coming down, as if singing a tune up there until they slowly reached the ground. It seemed to be telling me that it was okay for me to slow down too, that I should be like them: learning to take my time until the right moment arrived.

One ordinary day, as I was ready to face my daily routine, I got my first most important call here in Canada. I was offered a job that I already given up hope on. At that moment, everything around me changed. I started to notice that colors were springing up everywhere. Green leaves were starting to grow. Trees were coming to life. There were more people outside their houses. No gloomy sights in the neighborhood. And for the first time, I began to realize how friendly Canadians are: always ready to greet and smile whenever possible. It did not take long for me to realize that spring had arrived. It seemed to me that along with the growing trees and surfacing colors everywhere, hope came with them too.

On April 17, 2006, I went to the first day of my first ever job here in Canada. And every day from that day on, walking from the bus stop to the door of our apartment building every morning was like a breeze, especially now that I could wear my right shoe properly. Days turned to weeks, and weeks to years. Every step I take now is a familiar step. When I look around, I see a familiar place and familiar people. Canada, which once seemed like a big empty space for me, has now become a place for constructing new life and hope. Whether it's winter, fall, spring or summer, for me Canada remains a land which shows great promise. I knew that long before the colors in spring, long before the first job offer, even before my swollen toe healed, Canada had welcomed me.

Starting out is never easy. I went through times when I wished desperately for all those periods of starting out to come to an end. But in starting out, I learned that we don't have to rush things. I learned not to be so hard on myself because there is a right time for everything. Every hardship has its fruit. Every wound heals. And every winter has its spring.

 ROSSANA VELASCO lives in Winnipeg, Manitoba and has been appreciating Manitoba's generosity for four years. She came from the Philippines, where she was shaped to attain values of patience amidst adversity, respect and perseverance. She is passionately inclined in music, writing, reading and admiring people's talents. As a child, she was always moved by meaningful pieces of writing and beautiful music, and now she dreams that one day she will be able to make her own that can move people and touch hearts. She works as a laboratory researcher and color chemist. She obtained her Bachelor of Science Degree in Chemistry from her home country of the Philippines, where the people's affection and hospitality are as warm as the country's climate.

The Philippines is an archipelago of 7,107 islands. It is well known for its tourist spots graced with gorgeous beaches and scenery. The warm hospitality of Filipinos makes the Philippines one of the countries in Asia often visited by people from all over the world. Filipinos are known for their joyful and cheerful nature and their values of maintaining strong family ties.

Yard Sale

Jane Zhang

Winter is coming. It's getting colder and colder, and yard sales are becoming fewer and fewer.

I still remember the first time my friends took me to a yard sale to look for a bed and a dining table four years ago. The "hostess" was both nice and beautiful. She and her husband delivered the bed and table to our apartment after learning we didn't have a car. When she found we had nothing except the bed and table, she mentioned our situation to her aunt, who was planning to move.

Soon after, the 90-year-old aunt drove her car to our apartment and told me she wanted to give us all of her furniture. Three weeks later, the lady, her husband, her sister and sister's son drove two cars to my apartment. They helped move everything in and installed all of it with their own tools. I felt I had a home in a new country for the first time. From then on, I began to like yard sales.

Yard sales are a good way to improve my English. I usually begin a conversation with a simple sentence like, 'Please tell me what you call this? Could you please tell me what this is used for?' Sometimes even a small item will bring the sellers back to a sweet or unforgettable memory. Many of them like to share their stories.

Yard sales save me money. I have found a lot of useful things at very low prices from yard sales. I bought a nearly new web camera for two dollars, through which I talk with my relatives in my home country every week. I have used it for four years and it's been working very well. Yard sales offer a good way for people to avoid waste.

I learn about Canadian culture at yard sales. On a Saturday before Halloween I bought a piece of cloth from a couple to make a bag for my daughter. The wife said she could make one for me with her sewing machine. I left my phone number and waited for a call. Two weeks later I still had not heard back from her. I thought maybe she'd forgotten. If I were her, I might have forgotten, too.

Just before Halloween, I was very excited when I received the call. The woman had made a bag for me with her sewing machine. We became good friends after that. She is good at the computer, and her husband is a professional photographer. They have lots of nice pictures of animals like squirrels, birds and deer. They prepare food for the birds and squirrels in their back yard all year round. I can feel their love for animals, nature and life.

Every weekend during the warm months, I like to go out to yard sales, either looking for something unique or looking forward to a nice talk with people. I'll blend in with this culture more and more as time passes. Soon I will no longer be a newcomer. But I cannot forget the help I received during my first months here when it was a hard time being in a new country. And I will never forget what the ninety-year-old aunt said to me — that it was very hard for her when she immigrated here 50 years ago, so she was happy to do something for other newcomers.

HONG YAN (JANE) ZHANG was born in Northeast China. There are four distinct seasons and snow there in winter, just the same as in Winnipeg.

She currently works as an administrative assistant for Employment Projects of Winnipeg. She has a diploma in Business Administration from Red River College and a B.A. in Education from Liaoning University. She has met many new immigrants and is pleased to hear of their experiences, hard work and success stories. She worked as an ESL teacher for more than 10 years in her home country.

Note to Instructors

Thank you for taking the time to read these stories and sharing them with your learners. We believe these stories will resonate with your audience and lead to rich and meaningful language activities.

The activities have been designed for adult English as Additional Language (EAL) learners with a Canadian Language Benchmark (CLB) of 5+. Further these activities were developed for adaptation in the classroom; however many activities can be used by self-directed learners.

The story grid provides an at-a-glance overview of the types of activities, vocabulary, and CLB reading levels. The indication of the CLB is approximate as these stories are creative writing pieces and have not been edited to a particular CLB reading level.

We have included a range of activities to use in your classroom. The activities include: conversation questions, vocabulary exercises, reading comprehension questions, writing tasks, research activities, homework tasks, and grammar activities (dare we say it). The types of activities vary for each story so not all are repeated; if you see one you like please adapt it and share your activity with us.

In designing the language activities consideration has been made to include good practice techniques of pre-reading, while reading, and post reading activities. However, the sets of activities are not stand alone lessons and it is important to contextualize and provide scaffolding activities for your learners.

Thank you.

—*Iwona Gniadek*

Story Grid

	Story	Approximate Reading Level	Activities	Vocabulary
1	*Weyni Abraha's Story* Weyni Abraha	CLB 5+	Reading True/false • Vocabulary practice(Synonyms, Fill a blank, Paraphrase idioms) • Write a summary • Write a description • Re-tell story to a friend • Make a presentation	Regardless, betray, innocent, misery, powerless, breathless, drown, disappear, willing
2	*Next Chapter Please* Alan Balingit	CLB 6	• Reading • Write a letter of advice • Make a presentation • Class discussion	Gazing, anxiety, anticipation, adjusting, struggling, abundant, enigma
3	*You are the Master of Your life!* Iwona Gniadek	CLB 6+	• Conversation circle • Do a search online • Vocabulary game • Unscramble letters	Self-directed, independent, Self-sufficient, Autonomy, implications, voraciously
4	*Myeongsook's Poem* Myeongsook Jung	CLB 5+	• Teacher-directed conversation circle • Spelling of 'ing' verbs • Write an acrostic • Write a poem • Share a poem	Pursuing Stagnant Witch Spinning

	Story	Approximate Reading Level	Activities	Vocabulary
5	*Jill Lin's Story* Jill Lin	CLB 5+	• Reading comprehension • Make a glossary • Conversation circle • Word search—adjectives • Write sentences with adjectives • Write a bio • Write a description of a place	Impressive, incredible, graphic, successful, unforgettable, visual, social, traditional
6	*From +40 to –40: Why I Want to Write* Deepa Narula	CLB 7+	• Make a presentation • World quiz • Conversation circle • Write an email/summary/inventory/comparative essay	Exclaim, oscillating, notoriety, vicarious, self-directed learning, revolved, nepotism, dispose of, infuriated
7	*The Significance of Human Diversity to the World* Nathaniel's story Ondiaka	CLB 7+	• Find information about Kenya • Reading True/False • Paraphrase the sentences • Sort out the clues • Conversation circle	Vehemently, endow, adversity, cocoon, fashioned, surmount, curtail, envisage

	Story	Approximate Reading Level	Activities	Vocabulary
8	*Home: A Place of Sharing* Florence Okwudili	CLB 5+	• Conversation circle • Write about your favourite children's story • Translate and compare • Write a summary/comparative essay • Animals sounds in English and other languages • Describe how your pet is treated • Class debate—what makes a better pet: a cat or a dog?	Rooster, ushering, chirp, harmonious, flapping, frenzy, leftover
9	*Home* Daniela Rostova	CLB 6+	• Reading questions • Vocabulary matching • Insert words into sentences • Do a search on Macedonia • Describe your first home • Conversation circle	Adapt, belonging, afford, be attached, harmonious, wisdom, unknown, regret
10	*Spring Will Happen* Rossana Velasco	CLB 6+	• Make a presentation • Write about your first winter • Conversation circle • Hyphenated nouns • Write an email • Write a description	Well-developed, encounter, dominant, surfacing, breeze, heal

	Story	Approximate Reading Level	Activities	Vocabulary
11	*Home* Zulfiya Tursunova	CLB 5+	• Conversation circle • Make a presentation about the First Peoples in Canada • Interview • Word families • Fill a blank	Sorrow, joy, ancestors, ensure, quarrel, self-determination
12	*Yard Sales* Jane Zhang	CLB 5+	• Vocabulary Bingo • Unscramble verbs • Write a summary • Real-world assignment • Conversation circle	Hostess, nature, nurture, furniture, memories, waste

Questions and Activities

Weyni's Story
Weyni Abraha

Reading

Mark each sentence true (T) or false (F).

1. Both Suzie and Thomas were fatherless.
2. Thomas's mother was nearly blind.
3. Thomas wrote beautiful poems.
4. The mothers of Suzie and Thomas did not survive the escape from Ethiopia.
5. Neither Suzie nor Thomas knew what Uganda was.
6. Both Suzie and Thomas got jobs near where John lived.
7. Thomas discouraged Suzie from writing poems about hardships and war.
8. Suzie's uncle was able to sponsor her and Thomas.
9. Thomas died tragically on his way to Canada.
10. Thomas had not wanted Suzie to go to Canada.

Vocabulary Practice

Activity 1

Finish these expressions from the story.

1. Thomas worked around the *clock* to support his poor mum.
2. Suzie's mother said, "Our kids' lives are in our
   _____. We have to get them out of this
   disaster, or they'll have no future at all."

3. Suzie and Thomas ran like there was no _____ for several nights and days, not knowing where they were heading.

4. When Suzie came to the city to be with Thomas, he never took his _____ off her.

5. Suzie didn't want to leave for Winnipeg without Thomas. She told him, "I want to die with you, Thomas. Don't you _____ it?"

Activity 2

Paraphrase each expression from Activity 1. Write a sentence using your own words to illustrate the idioms.

Activity 3

One of the vocabulary building strategies is to replace words with their synonyms *(words that mean the same)*. It's not enough to find a synonym; you will have to check the new word in a dictionary to make sure it is used in the exactly same context.

Step 1

Complete each pair of words with a word that is similar in meaning. Choose from the following 10 italicized verbs:

fetch, giggle, escape, recite, pretend, deserve, struggle, surround, promise, suffer

1. pledge, vow   Example: promise=pledge=vow
2. chuckle, laugh
3. earn, merit
4. encircle, enclose
5. get, bring
6. recount, retell
7. endure, tolerate
8. elude, flee
9. fight, battle
10. act, make believe

Step 2

In groups or individually, look up the synonyms in a dictionary and decide which ones best replace the 10 italicized verbs above in Weyni's story.

Step 3

Fill in the missing verbs, choosing from the verbs above. You may have to change the form of the verb to fit the sentence.

1. Please, _fetch_ me my exercise book.
2. The starving refugees _____ to stay alive.
3. I _____ from insomnia.
4. A famous actor cannot _____ being recognized.
5. Suzi _____ her poetry to Thomas.
6. After she left for Canada, Suzi _____ to help Thomas.
7. After hearing the lousy joke, we all _____ at the joke-teller.
8. Nadia _____ to win the competition. Her story was the funniest.
9. Everyone at the table _____ not to notice the faux pas I had committed.
10. Let me explain some of the dangers which _____ us.

Step 4

Pick ten verbs that were new for you and write your own sentences with them.

Speaking/Writing

1. Write a summary of Weyni's story.
2. Write a description of one of the characters from the story.
3. Re-tell Weyni's story in your own words to a friend.
4. Find as much information as you can about Ethiopia and make a presentation to the class.

Next Chapter Please

Alan's Story

Reading

A. Skim and scan the text. In a group discuss the following questions.

 1. Look at the title. Read the first and the last paragraphs. What do you think the story is about?

 2. Take 3-4 minutes and skim the story. Were you right about your predictions?

 3. Alan quotes "The lure of the distant and the difficult is deceptive. The great opportunity is where you are." Who said the words? You have 30 seconds to find the answer.

 4. Who came to Winnipeg with Alan?

B. Read the text carefully to find details. Compare your answers with a classmate.

 5. In terms of professional career, is Alan's dream to make a lot of money or to regain the sense of achievement?

 6. Alan describes the opposite sex with humour. What does he say? Why is it funny?

 7. The expression 'faux pas' refers to behaviour or words that are a social mistake, e.g. bringing white chrysanthemums to a birthday. What faux pas did Alan allegedly commit? Have you ever committed a faux pas? Share your story with the group.

 8. What is Alan's former co-worker referring to when he says 'You are standing on it'?

 9. What does Alan's wife mean when she says 'seize them'?

 10. What do you think Alan's 'next chapter' will be about?

Writing

Write a letter of advice to Alan and his family about how to deal with various problems of settling in a new country. You may wish to focus on one specific area of life.

Speaking

1. Do some research and prepare one interesting fact about the Philippines to share with the classmates.

2. If there are students from the Philippines in your class, they could be interviewed by the group. They could also make a presentation about their country and its culture. What parts of the story can the students relate to?

3. What has been your biggest adjustment in coming to Canada? Discuss and compare with your classmates.

You Are the Master of Your Life
Iwona Gniadek

Conversation Circle

Note to teachers: Ask your learners to read the article and work on the answers at home before you meet to discuss them. This will help them activate their prior knowledge and experience, and facilitate/enhance their learning process.

OR

In a group, discuss the following questions. You can switch from a whole class discussion to small groups to pairs to discuss different questions. Debrief whenever you come back to the whole class setting by asking your classmates about what their findings are.

***Questions 3 and 6 *require doing some research at your local library or online.*

1. Learning English in Canada is different from learning English in your home country. What are the differences? Which way do you prefer?

2. Express in your own words, 'I am the master of my life and the captain of my soul.'

3. Who is the author of the quote? What did you find out about his life? Why do you think he said this?

4. 'Learning happens in the brain, not in the classroom.' Do you agree or disagree? Discuss.

5. How self-directed are you? List at least two things from your daily experience that you have learned on your own, e.g. how to change diapers, how to send an e-mail, how to fix the brakes on your vehicle.

    Work with a classmate and describe to him/her:
    - why you needed to learn this skill,
    - how long it took you to learn it,
    - how successful you became at performing this skill
    - where and how you searched for information about the particular thing (Did you employ the trial-and-error method? Did you do some research online? Did you go to a library?)

6. What is the Power Distance Index? What's the ranking of your home country? What are the implications of this ranking for you in Canada?

7. According to the author of the article, what are the two most crucial concepts that apply to all areas of life? Give specific examples of how you incorporate these concepts in your daily life.

8. Has the author mentioned any language-learning myths? Discuss.

9. List as many self-directed language learning ideas as you remember from Iwona's story. Which ones will you use from now on? Do you have any of your own ideas to add to the list?

Vocabulary Practice

Activity 1

Vocabulary review game

 A. To prepare for the game, pick 10 new words/expressions you have learned from the story and fill out the following table.

 B. Work in pairs or in small groups.

- Every group member makes one card for each word/expression
- Next, all cards in a group are mixed and put face down on the table
- Take turns drawing the cards. Do not reveal what you have drawn to others.
- Describe the word to your partner and ask him/her to guess the word.
- Whoever guesses the most words or expressions wins.

Word/Expression	Definition	Antonym	Synonym	Your own sentence
Self-sufficient				

Word/Expression	Definition	Antonym	Synonym	Your own sentence

Word/Expression	Definition	Antonym	Synonym	Your own sentence

Activity 2

Unscramble — Spelling practice

Unscramble the letters. All words appear in the text.

   a. *indentedpen*

   b. *creedledfist*

   c. *inflictfussfee*

   d. *iconspalimit*

   e. *mutilate*

   f. *laycoovirus*

   g. *entityvalet*

   h. *yuanmoot*

Myeongsook's Poem

Myeongsook Jung

Teacher-directed conversation circle and vocabulary practice

A poem is an arrangement of words containing meaning and musicality. Most poems take the form of a series of lines separated into groups called stanzas. A poem can rhyme but it doesn't have to, there is debate over how a poem should be defined, but there is little doubt about its ability to set a mood.

1. Discuss what a poem is. (It paints a picture before our eyes) Do you read poems? Who is your favourite poet? Have you ever written a poem? Do you know anyone who writes poems? If there is anyone in the group who writes poems, ask if they would like to share them with the group next time.

2. Put the poem title 'Myeongsook's Poem' on the board and ask learners to discuss it. What is the poem about? Who is Myeongsook? Brainstorm ideas.

3. Read the first stanza aloud. Ask learners to tell you what they saw before their eyes as they listened. Perhaps someone could draw a picture on the board.

4. Repeat the last line that ends in 'like me.' Ask the learners why she is comparing herself with the leaves. Why is she feeling like this?

5. Read the first two stanzas from the beginning, line by line, and ask your learners to repeat them aloud in groups or individually. Correct pronunciation if necessary. Display the two stanzas on a monitor or screen if you have one available in the classroom. Ask your learners what kind of a picture has been painted in front of their eyes. Is it static? Is it dynamic? Why? (verb+ 'ing'—progress/movement) and talk about how they create a dynamic picture.

6. Read the rest of the poem out loud. Ask learners to volunteer to read them aloud. Discuss each stanza.

   What does a baby represent?

   What does a witch represent?

7. Finally, ask learners to reflect on their own experiences and form groups for discussion groups. Just circulate and monitor the group discussions. Did they feel similar when they came here? Were they as determined as Myeongsook to succeed in their new lives? How did they achieve success? Etc.

Spelling Practice – 'ING' Verbs

Work in pairs and fill out the table. Add the 'ING' endings and put the verbs in the correct columns without checking the meaning of the verbs at this stage. Can you identify the three patterns? Take 5 minutes to complete the task.

Verb endings	?	?	?
spin	spinning		
go		going	
drink			
taste			tasting
talk			
leave			
study			
swim			
dye			
pick			
bother			
cycle			
type			
surf			

Verb endings	?	?	?
jog			
play			
annoy			
sing			
joke			
attract			
belly-dance			
cook			
echo			
eavesdrop			
fly			
hum			
install			
kiss			
lean			
nod			
ride			
veto			

Verb endings	?	?	?
walk			
x-ray			
yell			
zigzag			

Note to teachers: Debrief by showing the verbs line by line on the board (OHP, Smart Board) and asking learners which category the verbs fall into.

Acrostic Poems

An acrostic poem is very easy to write. It can be about any subject. This kind of poem can be written in different ways, but the simplest form is to put the letters that spell your subject down the side of your page. When you have done this, then you go back to each letter and think of a word, phrase or sentence that starts with that letter and describes your subject.

Note to teachers: Encourage your learners to work in groups and quickly write an acrostic using LEAVES or NEWCOMERS as the subject. Time the activity.

Writing/Speaking options:

1. Write a dynamic poem or story using as many verbs as possible from the above list.
2. Write a poem about how you felt when you first came here.
3. Bring a poem to the class and read it to your classmates. Tell them what it is that you like about the poem.

Jill Lin's Story
Jill Lin

Reading Comprehension

Read the story and answer the following questions.

1. Why did Jill learn how to play the piano?
2. What made her parents decide to send her to art school?
3. What benefits has Jill gained from travelling?
4. How would you describe her experience on Mount Fuji?
5. How might meditating help Jill in her career?
6. What does Jill say about graphic design that indicates that it is not just about patters of design?

Make a Glossary

A. Pick your favourite pastime and make a glossary of all the words that are associated with it. Do some research online or at your local library. Your glossary many include pictures, words, phrases, example sentences, idioms, etc.

B. Share the glossary with your classmates.

Conversation Circle

Discuss the questions with a friend, as a group in class.

1. Jill mentions playing the piano and drawing when she was young. What did you enjoy doing when you were young? Do you still enjoy these pastimes?
2. How do you feel about parents expecting their children to follow in their footsteps? Do you know of families in which this has happened?
3. Jill has visited several places. Where have you travelled? What benefits have you gained from your travels?
4. Jill likes to meditate. What do you do to relax or to clear your mind? How does it help you?
5. Bring a photo of a place you have visited and share your impressions with your classmates.

Word Search — Spelling Practice

Find the 25 adjectives in the grid below. Look horizontally, vertically, and diagonally. → ← ↓ ↑ ↘ ↗

Adjectives to find: cold, coldest, creative, crowded, deeply, different, dizzy, favourite, good, graphic, great, impressive, incredible, lovely, passionate, rainy, significant, social, strict, successful, tallest, traditional, unforgettable, visual, windy

```
E  Y  E  V  I  T  A  E  R  C  I  K  X  B  S
V  L  R  Y  N  R  M  U  X  Z  K  Y  M  T  O
I  P  B  Z  L  A  I  C  O  S  D  S  R  X  S
S  E  Y  A  Z  D  N  S  C  N  T  I  E  S  G
S  E  T  Z  T  I  C  B  I  E  C  G  L  Q  K
E  D  N  A  Z  T  R  W  H  T  H  N  U  E  C
R  U  E  Y  N  I  E  V  P  I  L  I  F  D  E
P  D  R  G  O  O  D  G  A  R  N  F  S  T  F
M  O  E  E  Y  N  I  A  R  U  F  I  S  A  S
I  X  F  D  Y  A  B  S  G  O  X  C  E  L  A
J  S  F  H  W  L  L  R  S  V  F  A  C  L  R
H  N  I  G  Q  O  E  B  L  A  G  N  C  E  X
V  R  D  X  U  A  R  V  S  F  P  T  U  S  W
D  C  G  D  T  B  O  C  O  L  D  E  S  T  I
P  S  M  F  J  Q  N  W  E  L  A  U  S  I  V
```

Writing

1. Pick ten of the 25 adjectives on the list above and write a sentence for each to show that you understand the meaning of each one. Example: Last year I had a strict teacher who wouldn't let us say a word in class unless we raised our hands.

2. Interview a classmate who is a newcomer to Manitoba and write her/his biography, using as many of the above-mentioned adjectives as possible.

3. What benefits can people gain from travelling to another country?

4. Write a descriptive paragraph about a place you have visited and the impression that it left on you.

5. Write about what you do to relax and relieve stress. How does it help you?

From 40 C to -40 C: Why I Want to Write

Deepa Narula

Class project

Make a presentation about India; the purpose of this project is to go on an imaginary trip to the country. The presentation should include pictures, videos and cultural stories showcasing India's history and beautiful traditions. The presentation could be accompanied by food sampling and perhaps some basic Hindi/Punjabi/Gujarati language training (for fun) if there are any learners who come from India.

This project should resemble a marketing pitch. Encourage the presenters to imagine they are travel agents trying to recruit as many tourists to visit the country as possible.

Options:

1. The above presentation can be followed by other countries' presentations of similar nature.

2. 'Who Wants to be a Millionaire?'—a world quiz

As a follow-up to the above presentations, learners prepare questions about their countries. Groups or individuals can participate in the game. For information on how to play 'Who Wants to be a Millionaire', go to www.google.com or your local library.

Conversation Circle

1. Deepa describes her first winter in Winnipeg. What was your first winter like? What advice do you have for classmates who haven't spent a winter here? What sort of things can you do in winter?

2. Deepa tells about having to get her driver's license in the winter. Where there any skills you had to quickly acquire when you arrived in Canada? Share your experiences with your classmates.

Writing

1. As a teacher, Deepa compares the education systems of India and Canada. Compare schools in your country to Canada.

2. E-mail or write a letter to a friend describing your first winter in Manitoba.

3. Imagine that your friend is planning to immigrate to Manitoba this winter. Email or write a letter to them to offer some helpful advice.

4. Write a summary of the following parts of Deepa's story:

   A. Her experiences while teaching in India.

   B. Her first winter in Winnipeg.

5. Deepa talks about the "inventory" of gains and losses she has experienced since she and her family immigrated to Canada. Make a similar inventory and compare yours to those of your classmates. What differences and similarities do you find?

The Significance of Human Diversity to the World
Nathaniel Ondiaka

Before Reading

Suggestion to teachers: Copy the bio and ask learners to read it at home. Encourage your learners to do a quick search on Kenya before the next class.

1. Read Nathaniel's bio.

2. Where is Kenya? What do you know about Nathaniel's country of birth? Share your knowledge with the class.

3. Read the title, the first paragraph and the last one. Think about what you have read and write down 5-10 words/expressions/ideas that you are expecting to find in the text. Compare your notes with a classmate.

While Reading — Are these statements True or False?

Skim through the story without using a dictionary and take no more than 15 minutes to complete this task. The statements are in a random order, not as the story goes.

1. Nathaniel's story is persuasive, not informational.
2. Both his parents passed away before he relocated to Canada.
3. Nathaniel is" nationality-confused" having lived in a few countries.
4. Having lost his wife to cancer, Nathaniel's Chinese father adopted him as a son; he's still alive and well.
5. Nathaniel does not see any advantages to the technological advancements of today.
6. The Global Village leads to isolation.
7. By 'CAB mentality' he means the fact that the Chinese offer taxi rides to tourists.
8. His marrying a Chinese girl was fervently disapproved of by both his parents and hers.
9. By 'better half' he means his spouse.
10. Living in a country of various tribal languages and cultures as a child, he had the opportunity to familiarize himself with most of these languages and cultures.

After Reading

Activity 1

Go back to your before-reading predictions (question 3). How many words/expressions/ideas did you find in the text? Were any of your words/expressions/ideas similar to the ones you found in the text?

Activity 2

Rewrite the following sentences using the words in brackets.

Example:

When Nathaniel has to face challenges of living in a new country, he does not panic. (faced)

Nathaniel does not panic <u>when faced with</u> challenges of living in a new country.

1. Some Canadians perceive immigrants as refugees.   (*perceived*)

   Immigrants _____ as refugees by some Canadians.

2. Nathaniel was not given permission by his parents to marry a foreigner.   (*disagree*)

   Nathaniel's parents _____ marrying a foreigner.

3. 'Congratulations on overcoming so many life challenges, Nathaniel,' his neighbour said.   (*congratulated*)

   His neighbour _____ on overcoming so many life challenges.

4. The pains, joys and dreams of each one of us manifested themselves in our written words.   (*demonstrated*)

   Our written words _____ of each one of us.

5. Upon graduation, my wife and I returned to Kenya to start a new life.   (*Having*)

   _____ , my wife and I returned to Kenya to start a new life.

Activity 3

Sort out the clues. Look at the completed crossword below. Can you find the word that goes with each clue? See the example.

								¹C	U	R	T	A	²I	L

Crossword grid:

- 1 Across: CURTAIL
- 3: REPLICATE
- 5: ENCOUNTER
- 6: PATRONAGE
- 7: FASHION
- 8: ENVISAGE
- 11: VEHEMENTLY
- 12: NURTURE
- 13: PREJUDICE
- 15: ISOLATION
- 16: IDENTITY
- Down: TRAVERSES, INTERNATIONALLY, ADDS, SURMOUNT, VEHEMENT, PREJUDICE(S), CONOCOON

A. when something is separate and not connected to other things _____

B. to make or do something again in exactly the same way _____

C. a safe quiet place _____

D. to stop something before it is finished, or to reduce or limit something   *1 Across*

E. to move or travel through an area _____

F. a difficult or unlucky situation or event _____

G. to deal successfully with a difficulty or problem _____

H. to help a plan or a person to develop and be successful   _____

I. in a strong and emotional way   _____

J. involving more than one country   _____

K. to make something using your hands   _____

L. to imagine or expect something in the future, especially something good   _____

M. who a person is, or the qualities of a person or group which make them different from others   _____

N. the support given to an organization by someone   _____

O. to experience, especially something unpleasant   _____

P. an unfair and unreasonable opinion or feeling, especially when formed without enough thought or knowledge   _____

Definitions taken from www.dictionary.cambridge.org

Activity 4

Conversation Circle—Interracial Marriages

Nathaniel is Kenyan by birth, but was adopted by a Japanese man. He studied in China, married a Chinese woman, and now lives in Canada.

1. Is there any mix of cultures in your family?

2. Are interracial marriages common in your country?

3. How has living in a multi-cultural country like Canada affected you?

4. Ask a Canadian neighbour/friend about his/her family background and report back to the class. Do many neighbours/friends have a multi-cultural background?

5. What are some of the challenges of marrying someone from a different culture?

Home—A Place of Sharing
Florence Okwudili

Conversation Circle

1. What is your favourite story from your childhood? Tell the story to your classmates.

   ***This could be a 'Stories of Our Childhood Day' in the class. Every learner or cultural group makes a presentation, preferably accompanied by pictures, of a children's story they grew up with.

2. Describe Obi's day from the moment he wakes up. How is his day different from your day when you were a child? How is it different from your children's day?

3. In your opinion, why is the mouse hiding from humans? Thinking of the environment, nature and Grandma Sarah's opinion of animals, do you consider mice to be rodents that need to be exterminated?

4. Grandma Sarah said that animals deserve the same treatment as humans. Do you agree with this statement? Support your point of view.

5. Do you have a pet? Is your pet like a member of your family? Describe how your pet is treated.

6. What makes a better pet—a cat or a dog? Have a class debate. Support your point of view.

7. Some people buy their children a pet to teach them responsibility. How can having a pet teach a child to be responsible?

Writing

1. Have you ever thought of writing a short story for children? If you don't know where to start, do a search online or visit your local library for information on how to write a children's story, make a plan of the story and all characters, and start writing. Good luck!

2. What is your favourite children's story? Is it translated into English? If not, translate it and share it with your classmates.

3. Translate your favourite children's story into English. Then, try and find a published translation of the story online or at your local library. Compare your version with the published one. Pay special attention to vocabulary choices, sentence structure and sentence length. Write a short description of between 200 and 250 words of what you have learned from this activity.

4. Write a summary of the story and tell it to your children at breakfast.

5. What grammatical tense is the story written in? Make a list of all the verbs used in the story and ensure that you know all of them. Write sentences that illustrate all the verbs.

6. Write a comparative essay on the cultural or generational differences between Obi's daily routine and your current one.

Reading

1. Read the story to your children. Ask them to read it back to you if they can.

   Alternately, have your children read the story to you first and then read it to them. Ask them to correct your pronunciation and intonation. Have fun with your children acting as your pronunciation mentors!

   After reading, discuss the story with your children. Together, retell the story in your own words.

2. Read the story in class as a group pronunciation activity.

3. What is the sound that chicks produce in English? What is the chicks' sound in your first language? Make a list of animals with their sounds in English and your mother language. Make sure you include all the animals from the story. If the sounds are different in English and your first

language, share some of them with the class and compare them with other languages.

4. How does Florence "humanize" the animals in the story?

Home
Daniela Rostova

Before Reading

Tip: Making predictions about the text is a reading comprehension strategy—Do not skip this part.

1. Take a look at the title. What do you think the story is about? Note down your ideas on the board in your classroom or in your notebook.

2. Who is Daniela? Where do you think she comes from? What do you think her life is like? Take a guess. Write down your ideas in your notebook. Compare them with a classmate.

While Reading

1. Number the paragraphs of this story from 1 to 7 before you start reading.

2. Read the first and the last paragraphs. Were you right in your predictions? What is the story about?

3. Read the next two paragraphs. What is Daniela's definition of home? Stop here for a moment. Do you agree with her? Discuss with a friend, as a group or with another classmate.

4. In Paragraph 3, she says she never owned a home. What does she mean by 'home?' Is she talking about a physical building or the sense of belonging?

5. Her first real home is here with her son and husband; it has a yard and a huge inflatable Santa who sits on the front deck during the Christmas holidays. Is this true or false?

6. What is the difference between cats and dogs regarding the feeling of attachment?

7. In Paragraph 6 she compares immigrants to migrating geese. Is this true or false?

8. She left her country because of cultural and generational differences between the young and old parents. Is this true or false?

9. Does she regret leaving her country? Explain.

10. Finally, what does she consider her new home to be?

After Reading

A. Vocabulary matching

Below are words and expressions taken from the story. Match them with the definitions on the right. When you are done, write a sentence using each word or expression. Ask your teacher, a friend, or another classmate to help you correct them.

1. to adapt	to be able to buy or do something because you have enough money or time
2. to be attached	the ability to use your knowledge and experience to make good decisions and judgments
3. to afford *EXAMPLE*	to gradually become an adult
4. to regret	not known or familiar
5. to grow up	someone's or something's place of origin, or the place where a person feels they belong
6. to come to mind	to like someone or something very much
7. harmonious	be remembered
8. unknown	to become familiar with a new situation
9. wisdom	to feel sorry about a situation, especially something sad or wrong or a mistake that you have made
10. home	friendly and peaceful

Definitions taken from www.dictionary.cambridge.org

B. Insert the words and expressions from Part A in the sentences below. Pay attention to tenses and word forms.

1. The situation for young people _____ in Poland in the 80s was far from peachy.
2. Her name _____ when you mention Macedonia.
3. "Don't I feel in my soul that I am part of this vast _____ whole?" *(War and Peace by Leo Tolstoy)*
4. "It is a characteristic of _____ not to do desperate things" *(Henry David Thoreau)*
5. Until she wrote her first novel, she was _____
6. Is there anything in your life that you _____ doing?
7. I cannot _____ to buy a bicycle this summer.
8. Have you noticed how quickly children _____ to the new situation after landing in Canada?
9. My sister is very _____ to her life, friends and family back home; she does not want to move to Canada.

Optional Class Projects

1. Do some research on Macedonia. Present one interesting fact to the class or your family. Show where it is on the map and tell them what you have learned about it.
2. Invite Daniela for an interview. Prepare questions for her in advance.

Writing Tasks

1. Describe your first home. What memories do you have of your first home (special events, etc.)?
2. If you could live anywhere in the world, where would you choose to make your home? Why?

Conversation Circle

Tip: Instead of a list, you can make an outline/drawing of a house and put the words in it.

A. With a partner or in a small group discuss and make a list of what you think makes a house a "home."

B. Compare your list with the lists of others in the class.

Spring Will Happen
Rossana Velasco

Group Projects

1. As a class/school make a list of Manitoba winter "Do's and Don'ts".

2. Make a multimedia presentation for your class/school about how to embrace each season in Manitoba.

3. Write about your first winter. Run a class/school competition for the most interesting/funny/moving story.

4. Review what the government page says about Manitoba seasons. Was there anything new for you on the page? Would you add anything to the page?

   http://www2.immigratemanitoba.com/browse/settle/choose-climate.html

Conversation Circle

Discuss the following questions with your classmates, friends, or neighbours.

1. For a moment, ponder Rossana's view of the new place through her eyes. What was it like for her? When did you arrive in Manitoba? How did you feel right after landing here?

2. What's your opinion about winter? How do you embrace it every year?

3. What new experiences does Rossana talk about in her story? Talk about the things you needed to learn or re-learn in Canada.

4. What is one of the reasons why Rossana was not hired? Did you hear similar reasons or others? Please share your experiences.

5. How long did it take Rossana to get her first job? How long did it take you? Was it the job of your dreams or a survival one?

6. Did you go through a lonely time like Rossana? How did you deal with it?

7. Discuss the 4 stages of culture shock. Can you find evidence of some of these stages in Rossana's story?

   ***Culture shock is the difficulty a person has while living in a foreign country. It is said there are four phases of culture shock: honeymoon, frustration, understanding and acclimation.*

   If you need more information on culture shock, do some research online or in your local library before you discuss this question.

8. Rossana uses a lot of proverbs in her writing. Discuss the meaning of the following proverbs:

   · Every hardship has its fruit.

   · Every wound heals.

   · Every winter has its spring.

   How do these three proverbs relate to Rossana's experiences in Canada?

9. What made Rossana feel like she was "inside a store that sells fragile, expensive items"? Have you ever experienced this feeling? If so, describe the experience.

10. What does Rossana mean when she says, "Every step I take now is a familiar step."

11. Rossana says that during her first winter her ears and fingers felt "a certain biting pain." What do you know

about the pain she experienced? What must people do in winter to protect themselves from this pain?

Grammar Circle

Hyphens are often used to create new words.

Remember to hyphenate all the words apart from the word you are describing, e.g.

A *sixteen-year-old* girl, a *two-storey* house

Look at the following examples:

We have a winter in Manitoba.   *six months*

We have a <u>six-month</u> winter in Manitoba.

Christmas is an experience.   *once a year*

Christmas is a <u>once-a-year</u> experience.

It's a kind of day.   *anything can happen*

It's an <u>anything-can-happen</u> kind of day.

Now, try these:

a. Rossana had a situation.   *swollen toe*

b. When Rossana landed in Canada, she   *wide empty space*
   had a strange feeling.

c. It seemed everything was an experience.   *first time*

d. She had an opportunity to come to   *once in a lifetime*
   Canada.

e. Rossana experienced cold during her   *bone chilling*
   first winter in Canada.

Writing

1. Write an e-mail to a friend giving him some advice about how to prepare for a Manitoba winter.

2. Pick an expression from Reading Question #1a and write about an experience you have had that illustrates this expression.

3. Write about the stage of culture shock that you are now experiencing. Use examples that illustrate the stage you are at in the process of acculturation.

Home
Zulfiya Tursunova

Conversation Circle — Poverty and the Homeless

1. When mentioning poverty, Zulfiya makes a reference to people living in cardboard boxes on the streets. What comes to your mind when you think about the homeless?
2. Have you ever stopped and talked to a homeless person? Have you helped a homeless person? If yes, how?
3. Do you believe in 'karma'?
4. Have you ever donated to a shelter or a food bank or visited one?
5. Are there homeless people in your country? How do communities help them (if at all)? How does the government support the homeless?
6. How does the province of Manitoba support the homeless? What organizations help them?
7. What are the reasons why people become homeless?
8. Do an online search for famous homeless people and present your case to the class.
9. After having the discussion with your classmates, has you own perception of the homeless changed? If so, how?

Writing

1. Describe the community where you grew up.
2. What is needed to create a sense of community?
3. Do you feel a sense of community where you are living now? Why? Why not?

Vocabulary Building

Part A

Word Families—fill in the blanks in the correct form of each word.

	Noun	Verb	Adjective	Adverb
1	production	to produce	productive	productively
2	a/_____ b/_____ c/_____	protect	_____	_____
3	identity	_____	_____	x
4	_____	imagine	_____	_____
5	_____	x	kind	_____
6	peace	x	_____	_____

	Noun	Verb	Adjective	Adverb
7	_____	restore	_____	x
8	_____	advocate	x	x
9	a/ relation b/_____ c/_____	_____	_____	_____
10	_____	_____	harmonious	_____

X = does not exist

Part B

Insert the words from Part A into the sentences.

1. This tree *produces* fruit every summer.
2. My umbrella offered me little _____ in the downpour last night.
3. Spies can never reveal their _____.
4. Children show great _____ when they play with building blocks.
5. We all appreciate random acts of _____.
6. I'm looking for a _____ place where I can work quietly.

7. Did you try to _____ that old piece of furniture?
8. We have to _____ for people who can't stand up for themselves.
9. My boss and I have a good working _____.
10. It is important to create a _____ atmosphere in the workplace.

Yard Sales
Jane Zhang

Vocabulary Bingo

Teacher reads explanations or descriptions while students look for correct matching words.

Suggestion to Teacher: Define all words and make more cards so that each learner has a different card.

Teacher's sentences:

1. One of the official languages in Canada
2. A place where some of us live
3. The season with lots of amazing white powder on the ground and ice-skating opportunities
4. Little gray animals with long fluffy tails very common in residential areas ·
5. A device used to make clothes
6. Family members
7. A set of qualities that defines a group of people
8. This happens when two people talk to exchange information
9. People we become close with, but who are not family members
10. Items used for sleeping in, sitting on, keeping clothes in
11. A sophisticated device used for transportation purposes
12. Unwanted material of any type

Students' cards:

nature	newcomer	waste	relatives
money	apartment	culture	furniture

money	newcomer	hostess	squirrels
furniture	waste	culture	yard sales

Halloween	sewing machine	waste	apartment
memories	camera	hostess	car

money	waste	deer	newcomer
nature	culture	yard sales	squirrels

apartment	waste	nature	table
relatives	conversation	hostess	yard sales

waste	furniture	relatives	culture
friends	sewing machine	English	winter

Unscramble — spelling activity

Unscramble the following past forms of verbs from the story

1.	ftle	11.	dover
2.	oughtth	12.	wandte
3.	oofrgt	13.	lpeehd
4.	rcvdeeie	14.	rhsdae
5.	saw	15.	tbghuo
6.	detargiimm	16.	stlldinae
7.	Draeh	17.	negab
8.	idd	18.	vased
9.	dsai	19.	kalted
10.	bceeom	20.	esud

Writing

Write a summary of Jane's story, using the unscrambled past forms of the 20 verbs above.

Real-world weekend assignment

1. Go out on the weekend and look for yard sales. Follow Jane's advice and start up a conversation with the owners. Perhaps have a list of questions that you would like to ask, but once you start the conversation, go with the flow and do not look at your paper.

2. Come back home and write an email to your teacher and fellow classmates describing the yard sale and any items that you bought.

   Option: write it in a text editor first (MS WORD) so you can make it as perfect as possible. Because the event took place in the past, ensure that your story is in the past tense and all the verbs have correct past verb forms. When you are done, copy and paste the story into an email and send it.

3. Read other people's stories, reply to their emails, and thank them for sharing their experience with you. Ask some follow-up questions to continue the conversation.

Conversation Circle

1. Are there many yard sales in your part of the city? How many have you been to?
2. Are yard sales a part of your culture? If not, why not?
3. Are there items you shouldn't buy at a yard sale?
4. What kinds of things do you prefer to buy new? Why?
5. Tell about the most interesting/unusual/useful item that you have bought at a yard sale.

ANSWER KEY

Weyni's Story
Weyni Abraha

Reading
1. T
2. T
3. F
4. T
5. T
6. F
7. T
8. F
9. T
10. F

Vocabulary practice
Activity 1
2. hands
3. tomorrow
4. eyes
5. get

Activity 3

Step 1

2. giggle
3. Deserve
4. surround
5. fetch
6. recite
7. suffer
8. escape
9. struggle
10. pretend

Step 3

2. struggled
3. suffer
4. escape
5. recited
6. promised
7. giggled
8. deserved
9. pretended
10. surround

Next Chapter Please

Alan Balingit

Reading A

Question 3—John Burroughs
Question 4—Alan's family

Reading B

Question 5 — to regain the sense of achievement

Question 6 — Alan humourously talks about how women's moods change

Question 7 — Alan's faux pas: answering honestly the how-are-you question instead of saying 'great, thanks'

Question 8 — bright future

Question 9 — when an opportunity comes by, Alan should go after it; catch it

You Are the Master of Your Life

Iwona Gniadek

Conversation Circle

Question 3 — William Ernest Henley http://en.wikipedia.org/wiki/Invictus

Question 6 — Power distance is the relationship between people in power and subordinates.

Question 7 — ownership and initiative

Question 8 — age-related

Activity 2

Spelling Practice

  a. Independent
  b. Self-directed
  c. Self-sufficient
  d. Implications
  e. Ultimate
  f. Voraciously
  g. Attentively
  h. autonomy

Myeongsook's Poem
Myeongsook Jung

Spelling practice

Verb endings	Last consonant doubled + -ing, e.g. spinNING	-ing added to the verb	The last –e of the verb is removed and –ing added
spin	spinning		
go		going	
drink		drinking	
taste			tasting
talk		talking	
leave			leaving
study		studying	
swim	swimming		
dye			dying
pick		picking	
bother		bothering	
cycle			cycling
type			typing
surf		surfing	
jog	jogging		
play		playing	
annoy		annoying	
sing		singing	
joke			joking
attract		attracting	
belly-dance			belly-dancing
cook		cooking	
echo		echoing	
eavesdrop	eavesdropping		

Verb endings	Last consonant doubled + -ing, e.g. spinNING	-ing added to the verb	The last –e of the verb is removed and –ing added
fly		flying	
hum	humming		
install		installing	
kiss		kissing	
lean		leaning	
nod	nodding		
ride			riding
veto		vetoing	
walk		walking	
yell		yelling	

Jill's Story

Jill Lin

Reading comprehension questions

1. Because her father wanted her to become a musician.
2. Jill's great results in drawing competitions
3. Travelling has enriched her life and broadened her horizons.
4. She had a headache, and felt dizzy.
5. It enhances creative thinking.
6. "…graphic design is a reflection of psychology and social norms. For example, different hues give people different feelings. A successful advertising campaign comes from a person's needs in society."

Word search solution

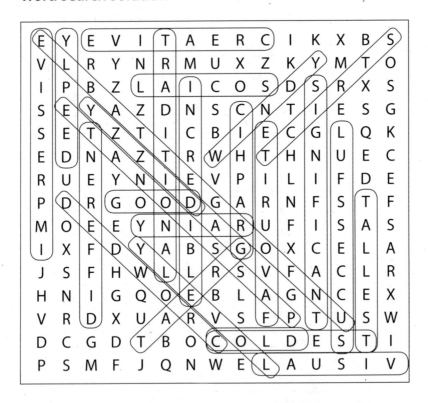

COLD	(8,14,E)	
CREATIVE	(10,1,W)	
DEEPLY	(2,6,N)	
DIZZY	(7,8,NW)	
GOOD	(4,8,E)	
GREAT	(9,10,SW)	
INCREDIBLE	(7,3,S)	
PASSIONATE	(11,13,NW)	
SIGNIFICANT	(12,3,S)	
STRICT	(15,1,SW)	
TALLEST	(14,8,S)	
UNFORGETTABLE	(13,13,NW)	
WINDY	(8,6,NE)	

COLDEST	(8,14,E)
CROWDED	(8,14,NW)
DIFFERENT	(3,13,N)
FAVOURITE	(10,13,N)
GRAPHIC	(9,10,N)
IMPRESSIVE	(1,10,N)
LOVELY	(10,15,NW)
RAINY	(9,9,W)
SOCIAL	(10,3,W)
SUCCESSFUL	(13,14,N)
TRADITIONAL	(6,1,S)
VISUAL	(15,15,W)

The Significance of Human Diversity to the World
Nathaniel Ondiaka

While Reading

Question 1—informational; he's just giving information about his life.

Question 2—false

Question 3—true

Question 4—false

Question 5—false

Question 6—true

Question 7—false

Question 8—true

Question 9—true

Question 10—true

After Reading

Activity 2

1. are perceived
2. disagreed to his
3. congratulated Nathaniel
4. demonstrated the pains, joys and dreams
5. Having graduated

Activity 3

A-15 across, B-3 across, C-14 down, E-4 down, F-9 down, G-10 down, H-12 across, I-11 across, J-2 down, K-7 across, L-8 across, M-16 across, N-6 across, O-5 across, P-13 across

Home
Daniela Rostova

While Reading

Question 2—'home' is a sense of belonging; it's more than the physical living space.

Question 3—a physical building

Question 4—false; Daniela refers to her first home while living with her grandmother. Santa used to visit her grandmother's place with gifts.

Question 5—Cats are said to be more attached to places, while dogs are more attached to people.

Question 6—false; geese are not mentioned in the paragraph

Question 7—true

Question 8—no; her home is the entire world; "I can go and adapt to live anywhere as long as there is peace, justice and basic needs."

Question 9—She considers 'the world' to be her new home.

After Reading

1h, 2f, 3a, 4i, 5c, 6g, 7j, 8d, 9b, 10e

1 growing up; 2 comes to mind; 3 harmonious; 4 wisdom;
5 unknown; 6 regret; 7 afford; 8 adapt; 9 attached

Rossana's Story
Rossana Velasco

Grammar Circle

    a. Rossana had a swollen-toe situation.
    b. When Rossana landed in Canada, she had a strange wide-empty-space feeling.
    c. it seemed everything was a first-time experience.
    d. She had a once-in-a-lifetime opportunity to come to Canada.
    e. Rossana experienced bone-chilling cold during her first winter in Canada.

Home
Zulfiya Tursunova

Vocabulary Building
Part A

	Noun	Verb	Adjective	Adverb
1	production	*to produce*	*productive*	*productively*
2	a/*protection* b/*protector* c/*protectionism*	to protect	*protective*	*protectively*
3	identity	*to identify*	*identifiable*	x
4	*imagination*	to imagine	*imaginative*	*imaginatively*
5	*kindness*	x	kind	*kindly*
6	peace	x	*peaceful*	*peacefully*
7	a/*restoration* b/*restorer*	restore	*restorative*	x
8	*advocacy*	advocate	x	x
9	a/relation b/*relationship* c/*relative*	*to relate*	*related*	x
10	*harmony*	*to harmonize*	harmonious	*harmoniously*

Part B

2. protection
3. identity
4. imagination
5. kindness
6. peaceful
7. restore
8. advocate
9. relationship
10. harmonious

Yard Sales
Jane Zhang

Teacher's sentences:

1. English
2. apartment
3. winter
4. squirrels
5. sewing machine
6. relatives
7. culture
8. conversation
9. friends
10. furniture
11. car
12. waste

Spelling activity:

1. felt
2. thought
3. forgot
4. received
5. was
6. immigrated
7. heard
8. did
9. said
10. become
11. drove
12. wanted
13. helped

14. shared
15. bought
16. installed
17. began
18. saved
19. talked
20. used